PELICAN BOOKS

A84

THE SCIENTIFIC ATTITUDE

BY C. H. WADDINGTON

THE
SCIENTIFIC
ATTITUDE

BY

C. H. WADDINGTON

PENGUIN BOOKS

WEST DRAYTON · MIDDLESEX

First published 1941
Second and Revised Edition 1948

*Made and printed in Great Britain for Penguin Books Ltd,
by Hunt, Barnard & Co, Ltd, London and Aylesbury*

CONTENTS

FOREWORD
TO THE SECOND EDITION

THE aim of this book is to point out some of the contributions which the scientific attitude of mind can make to the creative tasks of social reorganisation with which the world is faced. By this I do not mean merely an enumeration of new devices, new sources of power or techniques of production. The fundamental problems of to-day lie far more in the sphere of ideals and values—in the spiritual sphere, if you are not afraid to use that term—than in the technological. We already have all, or at least most, of the techniques we need to provide a decent civilised life for everybody. They are not yet producing that result, partly of course because the organisational machinery has been smashed in large parts of Europe, and partly because the old political and economic machine was unsuitable, directed to the wrong ends, and in obvious need of thorough overhaul, which unfortunately many people were not yet ready to give it. We have now to decide for what purposes the new organisation shall be designed. And to the discussion of these social ends, science has a good deal more to contribute than has been recognised hitherto.

I should be the first to agree that this is not a systematic treatise, every word of which is intended to be taken literally and subjected to the humourless mills of minute criticism. It was originally a topical pamphlet, written in those months, which already seem so far away, just before and after Dunkirk, before either Russia or America had been pushed into the war; a time in which the somewhat bleak prospect of the future made it all the more necessary to convince ourselves that we really had some positive values whose realisation we could look forward to. Why, you may ask, should such an ephemeral pamphlet be revised and republished? Because, I think, we have now come through to the time when the realisation of our ideals becomes a matter of practical politics. What during the war was an aspiration, is now relevant to the day-to-day workings of a democratic society at peace. The kind of influence which, I suggest, science should have on our social organisation is not one which can be simply grafted into the structure at one step, by the introduction of a single new piece of legislation. There is no critical point at which we must "introduce science" or all is lost. The true influence of science is as an attitude of mind, a general method of thinking about and investigating problems. It can, and I think it will, spread gradually throughout the social consciousness without any very sharp break with the attitudes of the past. But the problems for which it is wanted face us already; and the sooner the scientific method of handling them becomes more generally understood and adopted, the better it will be.

Many other people, in books, in articles, in speeches, in pubs and private houses, will have to take part in the discussion of our aims before the country as a whole has a firmly based objective. Each person will, and should, discuss his aims and objects from his own particular point of view, in relation to the field of activity in which he works and which he knows best. The views I put forward here come from a background of work in what is usually known as the cultural field. I am a pure scientist, holding an academic position in a university. The world in which I move is that of learning and research. This is rather remote from the life of most people, but it has a special responsibility to help formulate the common purposes for which the whole population is called upon to make such efforts. The members of the academic profession are the bearers and transmitters of the tradition of our civilisation, and they certainly can justly be called upon to say what they mean by it. What is important is not that they should state where they stand politically, and then give a view of culture as seen from that standpoint. Only if there was a scientifically assured body of political fact and theory would it be reasonable to take a political view as a sound basis from which to make a general series of deductions. At present this condition is not fulfilled. There are a certain number of large-scale political facts which can be accepted as certainly true—such things as the disorganisation of production and the existence of a standard of life much lower than our technical knowledge makes possible. Beyond these crude data, almost every statement is to some extent coloured by the presuppositions of the man who is making it. These prejudices, if they are to have any value, must be derived from a man's thought about his own life and work, on which he is competent to form a judgment. What one wants to hear, is the train of thought which leads from a particular sphere in which a man works to a political standpoint. That is what I have tried to give here.

I have tried to keep the discussion as much as possible to the cultural aspects of the problem, to what are nowadays known as ideologies. I am not concerned so much with particular economic or political remedies, but rather with the underlying ideas of what we are aiming at and what are the standards by which we judge whether a political or economic change is desirable or not. Until there is some agreement on these fundamental questions, discussion of particular problems is always at cross purposes and is only useful as a method of propaganda. I shall argue that science can not only solve special technical problems, such as the correct amount of vitamins to have in our bread, but that it has also developed an attitude to the world which makes some things seem valuable and others not; and these standards of the scientific world cannot be overlooked when the general problem of values is being discussed.

Perhaps I should, before going any further, attempt to pacify definition-addicts by giving some description of what

I mean by the word science. Let me say: *Science is the organised attempt of mankind to discover how things work as causal systems.* The scientific attitude of mind is an interest in such questions. It can be contrasted with other attitudes, which have different interests; for instance the magical, which attempts to make things work not as material systems but as immaterial forces which can be controlled by spells; or the religious, which is interested in the world as revealing the nature of God. This definition of science is only a very rough sketch of what the word really means. None of man's major activities, like science, art or religion, can be captured and pinned down on a dissecting tray with one single phrase. My idea of science, which other people may disagree with in some points, will only emerge gradually from what I have to say about it in the rest of the book.

It should not be necessary to emphasise that this pamphlet is in no sense a pontifical utterance in the name of science. The idea of writing it first arose at a meeting of a small scientists' dining club. Our motto is the old tag *Tot homines quot sententiæ*, as many opinions as people; this book is one of the opinions. It was not, of course, thought out in a hermit's cell, and I owe a great debt to my friends who have laughed me out of the more excruciating absurdities of the first draft, or suggested lines of thought I felt able to follow up. They include the artist John Piper, the novelist C. P. Snow, the architect Justin Blanco White, the scientists J. D. Bernal, Julian Huxley, J. Needham, A. F. Rawdon Smith, S. Zuckerman and the anthropologist Gregory Bateson, who, although he has had no chance to censor the book in manuscript, will probably recognise his ghost, misrepresented he may say, in its pages.

Although I expect every scientist to disagree with some of my opinions, and some with all of them, I think they are not mere matters of taste, which anyone can take or leave as they feel like. They seem to me to have a rational basis, to follow from the characteristics of the scientific attitude which are generally acknowledged. They are put forward as theses to be argued about and accepted or rejected on intellectual grounds and not on grounds of feeling alone. The claim that science has anything to contribute to the discussion of ethical or political questions, that is to say to the fundamental issues on which man's social civilisation is based, will probably be violently rejected by many most eminent and capable scientists; but I shall not be impressed by any rejection which does not seem to be based on substantial and rational grounds.

SCIENCE AND CULTURE

CHAPTER I

ON WHOSE SIDE IS HISTORY?

WE accused Nazism of being barbarism, a death to culture; we smashed it to the ground; but what do we offer in its place? We have been, I think, inclined to feel that Nazism is so beastly that there is no need to think out an alternative to it. We have held up our hands in horror as one after another of our cherished ideals has been flouted: at the persecution of Jews and other minorities, at the burning of books, at the legal changes which leave a man completely at the mercy of his judge's personal prejudices. But holding up one's hands is a gesture of surrender, and indignation is a very blunt weapon. Nazism will only finally be conquered when the whole social system which it produced is not only broken up but replaced by a better one which makes a stronger appeal to the people who live in it.

One of the first steps towards making such a system is to realise that Nazism did appeal to Nazis. The whole business of Winter Aid and concentration camps, the Strength-through-Joy and the Gestapo, the compulsory military and labour service, and the reduction in the number of students; the whole complex system which touched almost every point in the life of every German, did not appear out of the blue for no particular reason. It was able to come about because in most Germans there was something to which it appealed. This does not mean to say that the general mass of Germans got together in a democratic way and invented Nazism; they clearly did not. It is probable that most of the ordinary men and women in Germany would not, if left entirely to themselves, have undertaken the terrific labour and unpleasantness involved in many of the most important Nazi ideas, such as its desire for world dominion. But even this idea, with all the toil and suffering that it brings with it, appeals to something in many people—certainly in many Germans; and it was presented to them along with other ideals which probably appealed more strongly and, at the beginning, seemed more immediately practical and therefore more important.

A new system of social ideas, such as those of Nazism, does not have much chance to be taken up and put into practice unless people are suffering more than usually from the stresses and strains of life. In Germany before Hitler came to power many people were certainly unsettled enough to be ready for a change of some sort. Their difficulties were of two kinds, economic and what one might call general. Now of these two the economic may, very likely, be the more fundamental, and the intellectual cynicism and disintegration of the whole system of values and morals, which was so noticeable in Germany, may in the last analysis be a result of the misfiring of the economic machine. But for most people, things don't appear quite as the economists suggest. A man's economic difficulties are straightforward affairs, such as being out of work, or trying to cadge a living as a car salesman although he has an engineering degree. The connection between these circumstances and his moral and emotional troubles will probably be clear enough; his family life may break down because he can't afford to give his wife a decent home, or his son may take to drink, or more recondite vices, for sheer lack of anything else to do. But what is in theory important, and what in practice does not enter into one's ordinary experience, is the connection between social disintegration and the particular kind of breakdown which the economic machine is undergoing. It may, or again it may not, be true that you cannot have a system of lifelong monogamous marriages unless the economic system provides for at least a certain amount of private property. But even if it were absolutely true under all possible circumstances, nobody would know it as an immediate fact of experience. And if people are starting to recast the social system, it is likely that they will first decide that they want certain social and emotional things, such as monogamy or freedom of opinion, and only come later to the conclusion that they must have an economic order organised in corporations or limited liability companies or whatever it may be as a means of attaining their primary non-economic aims.

It is very important to remember that people may easily be mistaken as to the appropriate economic organisation for attaining their general aims. Such a mistake was made by the German people. The reason why they were willing to support Nazism originally was that they wanted certain things in their daily lives; some of these things, such as a system of established values which they could accept without question, and a sense of belonging to a community, they probably got; but others, such as a better standard of life, and security, they did not.

If is for these reasons—because non-economic considerations are a motive force in human behaviour in a more immediate and conscious way than different systems of economic organisation are—that it seems justifiable to discuss the modern world with an emphasis on its cultural aspect rather than its economic. By doing so I do not imply that the cultural motives were the most important for political leaders, as opposed to their followers. And it will be apparent all through the discussion that the two aspects cannot be at all sharply separated, and we shall come back later to the question of what the cultural requirements demand of an economic system that will allow them to be fulfilled.

The dominant characteristic of the cultural life of the world to-day is the existence of revolutionary movements. Communism is one, already over a quarter of a century old in the country of its origin, but still with its old fire in its newly conquered territories, and something not very different even in Russia herself. Nazism was another movement whose adherents, at any rate at the beginning, felt they were playing a part in a movement which would change the course of history. In England and America we know little of the vivid self-confidence and impatience of second thoughts which the revolutionary ardour produces; and little also of the difficulty for a single individual living in a community filled with this spirit to have any ideas of his own independent of those surrounding him. But in large areas of the world—perhaps the greater part of it—men are living in consciously revolutionary societies; and even in the more sophisticated and self-critical Western European civilisation, people have had a taste during the war of feeling themselves a part of an all-embracing social effort, and alongside the relaxation of going back to ordinary life, there is a feeling that things have grown smaller and of less consequence. Moreover we have seen a bit too much of the demerits of all the various revolutions offered to us—Nazism, Communism, 150% Nationalism—to feel much confidence in any of them. But a revolutionary set of ideas cannot, at least after it has attained a certain impetus, be defeated by a mere blanket of inertia. If Western Europe is to retain its old cultural importance in the new world of the future it must discover a new outlook to guide and animate its life.

The ideas on which our industrial civilisations have been run are breaking down everywhere, not only in Germany. They went first, and most completely, in Russia, in which a capitalist industrial system of the English type was in fact never fully developed. Then they were superseded in Italy, where again they had never been fully developed. The great slump of the beginning of the 1930's not only swept them out of Germany, but loosened their hold in England, France and America, where they were most firmly fixed. Who believes now that we shall ever return to the economic system and the social ideas of 1913? That world has gone; and we cannot oppose the chaos and anarchy of to-day by calling for a return of it. And yet, it is difficult to deny that

England now is a worse country to live in than it was then.

It is not only that before the war we were beginning to accept mass unemployment as nothing out of the ordinary, and were getting accustomed to the fact that in times of peace our productive resources are sometimes less than half used. But, with the acceptance of such a low standard of social efficiency, we were also tending to acquiesce in a gradual loss of social enthusiasm. Before the war most people were half persuaded that the old pride in being an Englishman was after all mere imperialistic jingoism, an unworthy attitude in face of the international problems of the day. That was perhaps in a sense true. But no society is worth much if its members cannot find something which makes them proud to belong to it. It is one of the conditions for the success of a new social order that it supplies something which fills this need, and it is one of the conditions of our survival that we shall find something which will make us as proud to be democrats as Nazis were to be Nazis.

There will never be any great enthusiasm for belonging to a society which is not going forward. And throughout England in the years before the war progress was at a discount. In almost all walks of life the way to get on, to reach positions of power and responsibility, has not necessarily been by the exercise of initiative and drive, or by showing an ability to seize opportunities and make the most of them. It has been at least equally useful to demonstrate that one knows the correct thing to do.

Our culture is full of unformulated rules of conventional behaviour, and we have placed a perfectly absurd value on the ability to conform to those rules, and thus to preserve the whole system whose behaviour they are supposed to regulate. A few years ago, many people said that one of England's greatest leaders in the last twenty years was the former Prime Minister Mr Baldwin, the late Lord Baldwin of Bewdley. And they said this, not so much because they believed that he created any great new values for us, or saved

us from any major disaster, but because of the way in which
he handled the abdication of Edward VIII. That is, what impressed them was Baldwin's knowledge of what would seem
polite behaviour in an embarrassing situation; just what note
to strike over the wireless, just how to bring the Dominions
into the situation, and what gestures should be made by the
Church and Parliament and House of Lords and so on. All
these things are actually perfectly trivial compared with facts
of economic organisation and international politics. Baldwin
is also the man who, running on a "Trust Baldwin" platform,
consciously misled the people as to his views on the international situation in order to reach a position in which he
could carry out a rearmament which he believed to be necessary; and, having reached the position, neglected to carry
out the rearmament to a sufficient extent. Only a society
which is completely sunk in formalistic politeness could consider that of less importance than the ability to handle the
ritualistic niceties of exchanging one king for another. England in recent years has been very dangerously near to this.
In little things, as in big ones, the man to whom responsibility
and trust was given was only too often the man of experience
in keeping things as they are and not the man of initiative in
improving them. During the war we did quite largely succeed
in getting away from this attitude; and the election of a
Labour Government showed that the country as a whole was
prepared to put ability and initiative before correctness. But
Britain is still, thank Heaven, a country of tradition; and it
is as well to recognise the dangers, as well as the advantages,
of that.

There is no denying, of course, that tradition has a value,
and a very high one. A great many people who felt like
running into a hole as soon as the air-raid sirens started up,
were kept going mainly because they knew it wouldn't be
the thing. And the refusal of England to panic at the time
France fell was mainly due to our stubborn acceptance of
the traditional idea that England doesn't get beaten. I doubt

if we should become hysterical, as many Americans did some years ago, at a realistic broadcast of an invasion of the world from Mars; such things just don't happen here. The strong belief which we still have that there are certain ways in which things should be done, and others in which they should not, is one of our strengths. But it becomes a weakness if the ways we believe in are too petty and rigidly fixed, and to some extent that is the case. We emphasised the importance of "correct" and traditional behaviour to such an extent that we almost lost the art of dealing with new situations which tradition did not foresee. Sometimes we get away with it by a sudden burst of initiative when things get really bad—our famous "muddling through"; it may come off, but again, as in the early part of the war, it may most definitely not.

It took several years of war before we learnt to sort out the really competent men, give them a reasonably free hand, and thus produce what the American Supreme Commander admitted to be the most efficient planning staff on our side.

The low estimation in which initiative is still held in England is probably hardly realised by most people who have never experienced anything else. But the contrast is very striking in America, for instance. People there are much nearer to a time at which initiative was a real social necessity and brought its own reward. When America was pushing out to the west and opening up new country, the drive and work of an individual who brought new land into cultivation or who founded a new business brought new wealth into the whole community; and the social values appropriate to those conditions are still recognised to a considerable extent in America, although the conditions of social life now are actually very different. As a matter of fact, a similar process of development must have gone on in England in a less obvious way. Our economic system was, in the early years of the last century, based on individual competition between small businesses, and originality and efficiency were qualities which an individual could show with his own resources; and they brought success, and were prized for doing so. Nowadays even in America there are hardly any empty niches left in which an energetic and competent man, starting from scratch, can raise himself to the top of the social pyramid; in spite of the ballyhoo about the "Land of Opportunity", the great majority of American labourers will remain labourers to the end of their days. And in England the independent producer has almost ceased to exist. The work of society is carried on, not by self-sufficient individuals, but by large firms and corporations. It is becoming less and less possible to set up on one's own except as a professional man or a shopkeeper, and even then conditions of work are very largely controlled by external authorities. Most people to-day have to enter a firm in a junior position as wage or salary earners; and getting on is not so much a matter of doing something real, with things, as of doing something psychological, to impress one's bosses.

It is probably not impossible to find a social system in which the integration of production into large units does not curb and frustrate the initiative of the men and women concerned. Certainly one must hope that it is possible, since there is no doubt that the integration is here to stay. In fact, it is clearly increasing all the time, and will increase further. The system of free enterprise of small units, whatever its merits were in the past, has been failing to work for many years. It failed even as a money-making concern, and we have seen a fairly rapid absorption of the small businesses into enormous combines and monopolies. The main driving force of these has been, of course, to make profits and distribute dividends; and they have mostly found that the best way to do so was to restrict output and charge high prices. But the need for centralised or monopolistic control has been at least equally clear when the purpose in view was production, as it may be in war, and not merely profit. In the last war the greater part of the economic system of the Allies was immediately put under fairly close government control, and as the war progressed we found it necessary to go even further in centralisation. It is clear that whatever happens we cannot return to unorganised small-scale businesses unless we are willing to put up with a very much smaller volume of production and a very much lower standard of life than would be possible to us.

The movement towards large-scale organisation of productive and business enterprises is so obvious, and has been so often pointed out, that it is hardly necessary to bring forward evidence of it. But it may be worth while quoting, as an example of a technical but non-political opinion, from the report of the committee set up by President Roosevelt in 1937 to report on the effects of technological changes on national affairs.[1] "A return to small-scale production methods in industry and agriculture cannot help but curtail technological progress at this period of history. Scientific research upon which modern technological invention is based has too many ramifications and is too costly to be undertaken and financed by small producers. Inevitably, existing technology, which is the primary contribution of the western world to civilisation, could not be maintained; its continuance has already met strenuous opposition wherever the theory or practice of small-scale production is current."

If business is organised on a large scale, many of the conditions of life will be determined by agencies whose powers extend over wide areas of the earth's surface. This does not necessarily imply that all governmental control must be even more centralised than it is now, and exerted more uniformly over the area which it covers. It is probably quite possible to centralise the administration of only the major aspects of policy, and to leave to smaller geographical regions, such as Scotland or Wales, more control over details than they have at present. Tendencies towards this kind of organisation are already apparent even in the highly centralised states such as wartime Germany and Russia. In the former there was a certain independence of the "Gaus" into which the country was divided; while in Russia the constituent republics of the

Union have a considerable autonomy in cultural affairs.

Even if some balance can be struck between centralisation and local autonomy, man cannot expect to return to the isolation and independence he used to have. In the old days a man could consider that his opinions and his intimate habits of life were nobody's business but his own. At the present day some one or other is continually getting at him to change them; either the government lays down rules as to what he should think, or newspapers, cinemas, radio, posters bombard him with suggestions.

This continual intrusion into what used to be considered the sacred privacy of the individual is again primarily a technological and only secondarily a political change. It can only be repelled, and the trend reversed, at the cost of discarding our modern methods of production. If we want to keep our lives inviolate, we shall have to go back to a civilisation in which we only meet our neighbours occasionally, after a long plod through muddy lanes to market.

These two results of technical development—large-scale organisation, and intrusion into the privacy of the individual —are, when they are given a political form, the hall-marks of what are usually called totalitarian systems. The meaning of this term is also coloured by our feelings about the countries in which such political régimes have been set up—hatred for the Nazi and Fascist systems, and usually at least scepticism about the Russian. But the objectionable features of these states are not inevitable accompaniments of totalitarian economic systems, as one can see from the fact that the three differ among themselves. The totalitarianism, on the other hand, does seem to be inevitable; the whole trend of recent history is towards it. One cannot dismiss the Nazis, Fascists and Communists all together for being, in their different ways, totalitarian; fairly soon we shall all be so, in some way or other. The Totalitarians of to-day have taken, with the wrong foot foremost, a step which we shall have to take to-morrow.

Instead of harping on their similarities, we should consider very carefully their differences. From a purely economic point of view, they present three full-sized experiments in possible methods of organising the productive forces of a country. If we have got to do that ourselves, as it seems obvious that we have, their preliminary efforts must provide a vast number of data from which most valuable guidance can be drawn. But this is a task for technically competent economists. From the point of view of the ordinary man, the Fascist-Nazi régimes, and the Communist régime, are two experiments in building social systems founded on organised totalitarian economics but with explicitly stated social aims which are completely different. Again there must be very valuable evidence about questions which one does not need to be an expert to understand. Is it possible, for instance, to combine totalitarianism with freedom of thought, or with initiative in execution? How can the most able men be picked out for authority?

Before we examine these systems to get what help we can from them, we must know what we want from them. It would be very unenterprising merely to look them over and select any features which happened to appeal to us. Their value is not as models to copy or horrid examples to avoid, but truly as experiments; that is to say as things which give us some insight into the causal mechanisms of social change and thus give us some power to control such changes and cause them to proceed in the way we desire. That is the essential nature of a scientific experiment. When Newton first passed light through a prism and produced a spectrum, he made a very pretty picture, all the colours of the rainbow. But the significance of the experiment lay not in the production of a pretty effect which other people could repeat, but in revealing something about the nature of white light, namely that it is made up of a mixture of light of many different colours; and this is important because it increased one's power of using light for other purposes which one may have in mind.

CHAPTER II

SCIENCE IS NOT NEUTRAL

MEN are, to a much greater extent than most of them care to admit, the products of the society in which they live. If you live in a slave-owning state, or a colony with an exploited native class, you cannot, even if you are nominally one of the free men, be on hail-fellow-well-met terms with everyone you meet, and treat him as your equal. The average Englishman of to-day cannot think and behave like an Elizabethan bravo or the average American like a Wild West cowboy. The impossibility of doing so is not merely legal; it is much deeper. A man's personality is moulded by the whole system of the society in which he grows up so that it fits in, somewhere and somehow, into the social pattern.

And the converse of that is also true. A civilisation is always being changed and added to by people who do not fit in absolutely smoothly, who think they could improve the society so as to make it better to live in. Until recently, the social conservatives had a guaranteed copper-bottomed rejoinder to such disturbing endeavours; modestly calling attention to their wisdom, they pointed out that their long experience (in one particular society) had taught them that men (in that society) always behave as the society considers right; you can't change human nature, they said. It was a fine argument while it lasted, but it no longer holds water. Anthropology, which is the scientific study of the societies which men have formed in different parts of the world, has discovered that human nature is an extraordinarily variable thing. The really innate qualities of men, the basic characteristics which society cannot change but must accept and build on, are much vaguer than anyone could have expected.

"Differences between one animal and another, between one individual and another, differences in fierceness or tenderness, in bravery or in cunning, in richness of imagination or plodding dullness of wit—these provided hints out of which the ideas of rank and caste, of special priesthoods, of the artist and the oracle, could be developed. Working with clues as universal and as simple as these, man made for himself a fabric of culture within which each human life was dignified by form and meaning. . . . Each people makes this fabric differently, selects some clues and ignores others, emphasises a different sector of the whole arc of human potentialities. Where one culture uses as a main thread the vulnerable ego, quick to take insult or perish of shame, another selects uncompromising bravery. . . . Societies such as those of the Masai and the Zulus make a grading of all individuals by age a basic point of organisation. . . . The aborigines of Siberia dignified the nervously unstable individual into the shaman, whose utterances were believed to be supernaturally inspired and were a law to his more nervously stable fellow-tribesmen. . . . A people may also, like the BaThonga of South Africa, honour neither old people nor children; or, like the Plains Indians, dignify the little child and the grandfather; or, again, as with the Manus and in parts of modern America, regard children as the most important group in society. . . . No culture has failed to seize upon the conspicuous facts of age and sex in some way, whether it be the convention of one Philippine tribe that no man can keep a secret, the Manus assumption that only men enjoy playing with babies, the Toda proscription of almost all domestic work as too sacred for women, or the Arapesh insistence that women's heads are stronger than men's. . . . We found the Arapesh—both men and women—displaying a personality that, out of our historically limited preoccupations, we would call maternal in its parental aspects, and feminine in its sexual aspects. In marked contrast to these attitudes, we found among the Mundugumor that both men and women developed as ruthless, aggressive, positively sexed individuals . . . approximated to a personality type which we in our culture would only find in an undisciplined and very violent male. In the third tribe, the Tchambuli, we found a genuine reversal of the sex-attitudes of our own culture, with the woman the dominant, impersonal, managing partner, the man the less responsible and the emotionally dependent person."[2]

I have given that quotation at some length because it is of the very greatest importance to realise that human nature is plastic, and can be shaped by society either for good or ill. If man were really an unregenerate and unimprovable brute, there would be no point in any cultural activities, or even in discussing the changes which could be made in society; what would be the purpose of making them if man himself became no better because of them? But such pessimism is unjustified; even those qualities of man which we usually consider the most spiritual, his unselfishness, his striving, his love for his fellow-men, can be altered and improved by changes in the social system in which he lives.

The present is one of those periods when society is being rapidly and profoundly altered. There are probably few people in Europe who feel that they fit in well to our system, with its wars, unemployment and general chaos; and it is obvious in all directions that changes are occurring. The development of society may take place in a more or less haphazard way, as a result of a multitude of small adjustments to particular evils, uncoordinated by any general point of view. But it would be more sensible if the people who find that they have outgrown the ways of life which society has tried to force on them decided first of all to discover what sort of people they wished to be, and then worked out what sort of society would allow them to be like that.

It may seem at first sight that it is quite obvious what the desirable qualities in a man are. It is easy to run off a list of virtues—energy, tolerance, creativeness and so on. But when we do so, we are usually thinking of these qualities within our present social framework, with all the presuppositions which it involves. When the framework gets out of date, and the system starts misfiring, it becomes less obvious which are the desirable attributes. The recent systems of Germany and Russia have certainly chosen some which we have not particularly valued—a ruthless devotion to the state in Germany, for example, and an equally selfless dedication to a particular concept of human progress in Russia.

But the seeds of the new life are here among us; there is no need, even if it were possible, to start out from scratch to invent a new ideal type of man. As our society has changed, and the conventional virtues have been frustrated, like enterprise, or gone out of date, like thrift, or even become social dangers, like competitiveness—all this time, the conditions of a new life have been developing, and the virtues which would make it possible to extract the greatest benefit from those conditions have become clearer. The people who, above all others, are interested in charting the development of human possibilities are the writers and artists. The function of culture is not, as many think, to enrich human life with new conceptions which it draws from some mysterious and transcendental realm out of the reach of ordinary people. The true, or at least the most important, task of the cultural worker is to reveal to man the spiritual riches which would result from the full exploitation of the immediately practical possibilities. The culture of Greece laid bare the greatest heights to which a slave society could aspire; that of the Renaissance worked out the potentialities of the newly-discovered learning in the circumstances of its own period of history. It is an exaggeration of this point of view to claim that the material conditions of existence determine the nature of culture. But they do limit it. The state of technical knowledge, and the balance of social forces, gives man his opportunity. It is up to him to make the best of it; and in this endeavour it is the writers and artists, the scientists and architects who act as scouting parties to explore the terrain in front of the main body of the advance. It is from present-day culture that we can learn what sort of being modern man should be, and it is only when we know this that we can decide what political and economic system we must try to create.

In the past, artists and writers were able to perform alone this prime function of culture, the adaptation of man's ideals to the material world in which he lived. At present that is no longer true; they need to be joined by the scientist. Until about two hundred years ago, the material conditions of daily life changed very slowly. The new potentialities of life, which gradually arose, and which it was the duty of cultural activity to reveal, depended on changes in the economic organisation of society; the change from city states to empires, from slave civilisations to feudalism, or from feudalism to trade and capitalism. It may be true, as one school of historians assert, that in many cases these transitions were ultimately due to technical advances in handling the raw materials of life; for instance the breakdown of feudalism may have been connected with the recruiting of large labour forces for working mines or mills using water power. But these technical improvements can at most only have acted as the last straws, the triggers which released a sequence of alterations which affected the lives of many people who had no direct or immediate contact with them. The psychological and cultural problems made themselves felt not in terms of material techniques but in connection with the changes in economic status. The technical man had no special appreciation of them, and no special contribution to make to their solution.

Nowadays the whole setting of our problems is obviously quite different. Everyone recognises that the difficulties which are shaking loose the old framework of civilised life are the results of technological changes. These act in two ways. New inventions and new processes have rapidly changed the day to day life of ordinary people; cars, electric light, telephones, radio and so on have made a world in which an adult man of Shakespeare's day would have difficulty in surviving for a week. And other technical advances, which do not enter directly into the experience of most people, have necessitated very great changes in the economic structure of society, and thus affect everyone at second-hand. The increase in size of the productive units—factories, firms, corporations, etc.—which carry on the business of the world is perhaps partly due to the inherent processes of capitalist economy, but it is also something more than a merely economic phenomenon; it is dictated by modern technological methods, and would occur under any economic system in which these methods could be used. Man, unless he is willing to give up the advantages of mass production and large-scale operation, can never again be his own master in the way a medieval craftsman was. And if civilisation is to continue to advance, and if full use is to be made of the opportunities for a richer life which technical advances present, the scientist and technician must join with the artist and writer in thinking out what those possibilities are and bringing them to the notice of people in general.

Up to the present, the collaboration of scientists in the general cultural activities has been very flimsy. They have mostly been content not to challenge the verdict passed on science many years ago by the encrusted incumbents (Beaune from the neck up) of ancient Professorships: that science is "stinks" and has nothing to tell the humanities. The general adoption of this valuation by the cultivated world was the penalty which science paid for being allowed inside the privileged circle of the Universities.

In the seventeenth century it did not compete with Classics, Theology and Metaphysics for academic veneration and the easy existence of an endowed Chair, but it made no pretence that it was indifferent to its effect on social life. The Royal Society, the most august of English scientific bodies, was founded in 1662 by a group of men who snared the belief expressed by Boyle in the words "the good of mankind may be much increased by the naturalist's insight into the trades," and many of whom had earlier come together in a society, the Invisible College, which "values no knowledge but as it hath a tendency to use." They were not all scientists as we now understand the term, but included also men like Wren, the architect, and Samuel Pepys, now famous for his diary but then an important administrative official in the Admiralty. At rather earlier periods, the examples of Sir Thomas Browne and Leonardo da Vinci are two very different instances of the way in which scientific and cultural interests and achievements were combined in the same man. Nowadays it would be only slightly unfair to take as typical of the relations between science and the arts the reviews of the Royal Academy which appear each year in *Nature*, the most widely read English scientific journal; very meticulously, the reviewer notes whether the geology of the landscapes, and the anatomy of the young ladies, is sufficiently text-book.

This decay of the relations between science and culture, and the concomitant withdrawal of science into the purely technical sphere, is often supported by the specious and ambiguous argument that science is, and must be, ethically neutral. In its most trivial and individualistic sense, that scientists do not mind which way their experiments come out, this is clearly untrue; nearly all active scientists more or less passionately hope to be able to prove or disprove some particular theory on which they are working. But that is irrelevant to the function of science as a cultural force. It is much more important that scientists must be ready for their pet theories to turn out to be wrong. Science as a whole certainly cannot allow its judgment about facts to be distorted by ideas of what ought to be true, or what one may hope to be true.

It cannot, for instance, allow its estimate of the relative food values of animal and vegetable foodstuffs to be influenced by the ethical arguments for vegetarianism. But it is stultifying and misleading to state that science can merely measure the advantages of the different animal proteins over the vegetable ones, and must then leave the ethical question entirely on one side, to be decided by others. The food values of various kinds of nourishment are an essential part of the whole situation on which an ethical judgment has to be made, and a part which, without the aid of science, we should remain ignorant of. If, or perhaps one should say when, science discovers some alternative and equally simple method of producing the food mankind needs, we shall quite likely think it more suitable to give up the somewhat inelegant apparatus of stockyards and slaughter houses on which we depend at present.

The contribution which science has to make to ethics, quite apart from questioning its fundamental presuppositions, but merely by revealing facts which were previously unknown or commonly overlooked, is very much greater than is usually admitted. The adoption of methods of thought which are commonplaces in science would bring before the bar of ethical judgment whole groups of phenomena which do not appear there now. For instance, our ethical notions are fundamentally based on a system of individual responsibility for individual acts. The principle of statistical correlation between two sets of events, although accepted in scientific practice, is not usually felt to be ethically completely valid. If a man hits a baby on the head with a hammer, we prosecute him for cruelty or murder; but if he sells dirty milk and the infant sickness or death rate goes up, we merely fine him for contravening the health laws. And the ethical point is taken even less seriously when the responsibility, as well as the results of the crime, falls on a statistical assemblage. The whole community of England and Wales kills 8,000 babies a year by failing to bring its infant mortality rate down to the level reached by Oslo as early as 1931, which would be perfectly feasible[3]; but few people seem to think this a crime.

Quite recently, a new problem has arisen as the greatest conundrum facing the ethical judgment of man—the problem of the atomic bomb. Here it is inescapable that scientists must play a large, if not a dominant, role in deciding how man's new powers should be incorporated into his social life. Their responsibility is very large merely because of their knowledge. Anyone, endowed with the normal human ideas of right and wrong, can see that the bomb should be used as little as possible—though it is pertinent to point out that it was the scientists, not the non-scientific men, who protested against its use at Hiroshima and Nagasaki before the Japanese had been warned. When it comes to drawing up detailed measures to prevent resort to the bomb, it is only men with considerable scientific training who can appreciate the effects of various courses of action. Any system of control will come into some sort of conflict with the ideas of nationalism in which, unfortunately, so many of man's deepest ethical beliefs are nowadays involved. It is only scientists who are in possession of the information and theoretical understanding which can make it possible to decide on a system of control which conflicts as little as possible with other legitimate social values. There is no possibility for the physicist to fail to recognise his responsibility; and no excuse for non-physicists to deny the paramount importance of his counsel. And all this is true even if the scientist accepts without question the system of ethical values current in his time and his society.

But the ethical implications of a scientific attitude go even farther than this. The maintenance of a scientific attitude does in fact imply the assertion of a certain ethical standard. The reason that this has been overlooked, or denied, is that the scientific attitude consists in the overruling of the more obvious emotions which might interfere with the unbiassed appraisal of the situation; and the old-fashioned psychology which made a sharp distinction between the "faculties" of thinking and feeling seemed to lead to the conclusion that science must banish all feeling and thus all ethical judgment. With the recognition in more recent times that such a distinction is unjustified, that all acts involve both feeling and thought, it becomes theoretically impossible to deny that "feeling" is an element in the scientific attitude. Observation of the behaviour of scientists in their corporate and professional capacity confirms this. Before the war there was a very remarkable agreement among scientists throughout the world that a system of thought such as Nazism is incompatible with the scientific temper and is, for that reason among others, to be ethically condemned. Expressions of this point of view can be found in all the general periodicals of scientists, such as the English *Nature* and the American *Science*, with the exception of course of the officially controlled press of the Nazi or Fascist countries; and in the latter, the assertion of the ethical consequences of the scientific attitude has, as is well known, been made by many individuals who have suffered for doing so.

It is time, in fact, that scientists become willing to state explicitly that the scientific attitude is as full of passion, as much a function of the whole man and not merely of an intellectual part of him, as any other approach to human action. It differs from them only in what it is trying to do. Instead of trying to earn more money, or to improve the condition of the working class, or to create visual beauty, a scientist tries to find how things work. The search for causal connections cannot be made merely by refusing to grind axes. Scientific imagination and insight do not automatically result when the mind is swept clean of preconceived notions and prejudices; their attainment is a positive achievement and not a merely negative one. And because this is true, scientists can and do pass ethical judgment on human behaviour; those things which are based on the scientific attitude, or encourage it, are good, those which stultify or deny it are to that extent bad.

Finally, a more debatable, a more philosophical, and a

SA–B

less immediately important point: the scientific outlook has its own appropriate intellectual approach to the fundamental problem of deciding which, of the numerous and varied ethical beliefs man has held, is the best. There is no space or necessity to discuss this matter in detail here.[4] Roughly, the argument is that men's ethical beliefs influence their actions, and that one can observe these effects, and thus form a scientific theory as to the functions which ethical ideas fulfil in human life, just as one can form a theory of what function foods fulfil. Such a theory, I think, would have as its main thesis that the most important function of men's ethical beliefs is to provide a powerful mechanism by which human evolution is carried forward. If that is so, those ethical ideas which are most satisfactory in helping man along the path of evolution could be judged to be "the best", in exactly the same sense that "the best foods" are those which most satisfactorily fulfil the needs of his normal growth and development. Before one can make any practical use of this philosophical theory, of course, one must be able to discover at least the main outlines of the course of evolution—a difficult task, and one which must be approached without any narrow prejudices to look only for the obvious material factors, but a task which is no more difficult than that required by any other way of considering the eternal problems of right and wrong.

In the recent past, although science has been commonly held to be ethically neutral and unconcerned with politics and social affairs, the scientific spirit has in fact been making an important contribution to the development of general cultural ideals. The goals towards which a society is moving are not always, perhaps not ever, completely conscious and formulated even by the most far-sighted individuals. A movement as powerful as science has been in our civilisation is bound to affect, even if unconsciously and at second-hand, the outlook of all those concerned with any aspect of the society's culture. We shall find, in fact, that an examination of recent artistic movements reveals a number of close connections with the scientific attitude of mind. The most constructive artistic outlook of recent times is one which shares very many of the characteristics of the scientific mentality; so much so that in Nazi Germany it fell under the same ban. The best of modern art is compatible only with true science, and a bogus science requires a fake art to keep it company.

In the next three chapters I shall therefore do my best to exhibit the cultural influence of science at the present day. It has recently become fashionable, when discussing the social influence of science, to put the emphasis on earlier periods of history—the geometry of the Egyptians, the astronomy of the Babylonians, and the ballistic problems tackled by the Renaissance mathematicians. But history is a heap of data in which one can bring to light examples to prove almost any theory one wishes; and when one has found a nice example, only the most self-confident specialist has any means of judging whether it holds water. No amount of palaver about the largely hypothetical past is a substitute for an analysis of the present, which can be checked by direct experience.

The study of the present, rather than the past, relations between science and society is the more essential nowadays because they have changed so considerably in recent times. In the past science was a comparatively minor activity of man, and the problems it tackled, and the course of development it followed, were to a very large extent dictated to it by man's other social activities. The social control over science is still a fact; a very penetrating and comprehensive analysis of it has been published by Bernal in his *Social Function of Science*. But science is now no longer so passive; it has acquired a momentum and strength of its own. Far from being content merely to accept the problems society suggests to it, it finds that it must pose problems to society. The thesis I want to argue is that science is already a very potent social force, and that it has certain social requirements on whose satisfaction it must insist.

CHAPTER III

ART BETWEEN THE WARS

THE majority of artists, and those who become most popular, express the feelings and ideas which belong to the recent past or the immediate present. The ordinary man recognises himself in their works, and likes it. But the artists who shape the world to come are those who see a bit further than other people, who point out new ways, and force their message across, to some extent at any rate, on to a lazy and unwilling public. They are the creators, who do something more than reflect their surroundings.

In the past, when events moved at a more decorous speed, it usually took a really original artist or poet about twenty or thirty years to become widely understood. To-day, with the world in a wild stampede, the mediocre artists are far behind the general public, and the creative ones far in front. The conditions of life with which they are dealing are not, at the most generous estimate, more than twenty years old; there has simply not been time enough to assimilate the problems of modern life, to create some æsthetic solution of them, and to get that solution generally accepted. So there are no acknowledged representative modern artists and poets; most of the men who come into question, and whose work deals with the world as it is now, are still young and still in the stage of being called cranks. The works which I shall discuss may seem queer, but at any rate they pass two of the tests of public esteem; the highbrow and the lowbrow. They would be, I think, considered important by the professional critics of modern culture; and they do, within the range of goods they represent, fetch high prices. Picasso probably commands more per square inch than any other painter ever did whilst still living. Neither of these criteria will satisfy the middle-brows, but as they are mainly concerned that things should not be too extreme, their opinion may be worth having about what is good art, but is not important when one is considering, as I wish to, in which direction art is going, dragging society behind it.

For a somewhat similar reason, I shall not discuss novels or the cinema. In some ways they are the most important arts of the present day, but they are not the most indicative. They are the arts which keep in closest touch with ordinary life. In novels the new ideas, whether original or borrowed, are worked in with the great mass of human characteristics which gives life its continuity; and although they are thereby reinforced and given body, they are, from another point of view, diluted and made less easy to recognise. If one compares a whole culture to a valley, the novels are the great rivers of the plain, on which the traffic flows; but the same slope of the land is more obvious up in the uncouth hills where the little streams, the poetry and painting, make a great clatter but gather no moss.

The meaning of a work of art is as difficult to describe as the expression of a human face or the song of a bird. The words of everyday prose are too crude to convey what the artist or the poet means; otherwise he would have used them. The enormous labour a creative worker puts into a painting or a poem is not done just for fun, fun though it may sometimes be; and the apparent strangeness which the result generally has for his contemporaries is not due to his perversity, but to the fact that he is trying to convey something which is new and therefore, since he has not had time to think it out fully, complex. But when one is considering, as we are, the importance of artistic movements for the social strivings of an epoch, one need not be bothered with the most troublesome of all questions about art. There is no need to consider how to judge the ultimate value of a work of art, or which are the best artists. The aspects of art or poetry which we shall be considering here are almost independent of æsthetic value. Some people—the believers in Art for Art's sake—would say that the value of a poem or picture is completely disconnected from its meaning; they claim that the only thing which is significant æsthetically is the mysterious magic for which we can give no recipe, but which we can recognise as the quality which differentiates poetry from verse or a picture from a mere representation. Personally, I think this goes too far; I do not believe that a man can be a really great artist unless his pictures contain not only the purely æsthetic magic, but also some attitude, of a generous and large-scale kind, to important aspects of human life. But certainly one cannot judge the value of artists merely by their social outlook; and that is why a discussion of the influence of artists on their contemporaries must largely disregard their ultimate æsthetic value as later generations recognise it. If artists were nothing but creators of visual magic, we could neglect them as an influence on the direction in which society develops; but they are not; the æsthetic power is a bait which, when accepted, carries with it all kinds of comments on the life by which the artist is surrounded and which intrudes itself, whether he will or not, into his work. For later generations, this may be comparatively unimportant, but for those who live at the same time and place, it is this intrusive "meaning" which constitutes much of the artist's importance.

From the social point of view, the importance of an artist is not only measured by the number of people, interested in art, who think him good, but also by the effect he has on the artistic surroundings of the ordinary man who is under the mistaken impression that he never looks at a work of art from one year's end to another. The latter category is very important. Everybody, whether or not he ever goes to picture galleries or reads highbrow literature, is continually seeing posters and films, and reading the prose of advertisements and newspapers. A poster or advertisement of ten years ago looks obviously out of date to-day (except for patent medicine advertisements, which are nearly always designed to look ten years out of date anyhow, since they are aimed at older people with old-fashioned ideas). This passé appearance of the popular art of a few years ago shows how rapidly public taste changes. And it does not change because of some occult law of nature, but as a result, finally, of the creative work of highbrow artists. The man in the Underground may never have seen a picture by Picasso, and if he did, might dislike it; but he would not regard it with quite the same blank incomprehension or shocked hatred as did his father, who had never sat opposite a watered-down Picasso advising him to Go By Underground—It's Quicker.

The artists themselves know very well that they are the people who bring about the changes in popular taste. Struggling as they usually are to make both ends meet, they must often be tempted to give up the trouble of being a jump ahead of the rest of the world and to start earning the fat salaries of the people who adapt last year's artistic ideas to commercial purposes. If the only result of their creative activity was to alter the general lay-out of advertisements or the prose style of casual writers, there would be no important reason why they should go on with it. But most of them realise more or less consciously that these things are merely symbols of more important changes. Writing and pictures are methods of conveying ideas or feelings, and one cannot alter their character without altering the thoughts behind them. The sonorous and weighty sentences of a Victorian, with the adjectives descending from Olympian heights in neat squadrons of three, and the subordinate clauses rolling irrefutably after each other like the waves of a regular periodic function, belong to an age when one expected people to believe what one had to say. Nowadays we feel we ought to provide sixpennyworth of cracks, and you can laugh at the rest gratis if you want to. Measured utterances have disappeared from present-day use because our thought, more turbulent and contradictory, more ready to apprehend something of which it had been previously unaware, does not fit into that form. Their disappearance is deeply connected with our change to a society in which the comfortably-off have orange juice before breakfast instead of family prayers.

It is usual to quote Plato as an authority for the view that the ideas of poets and painters eventually get across to their contemporaries and modify the basic assumptions on which their way of life is founded. It is more important to find that the artists themselves express the same thing. Although Picasso has devoted his whole life to painting furiously in his studio without apparently caring in the slightest what the world thinks of the results, he has probably had as great an influence as any living man on the kind of approach to the world which the Englishman, Frenchman or American finds interesting. And, on one of the few occasions on which he is recorded as having said anything, what he said was:

> "We might adapt for the artist the joke about there being nothing more dangerous than instruments of war in the hands of generals. In the same way, there is nothing more dangerous than justice in the hands of judges, and a paint-brush in the hands of a painter! Just think of the danger to society! But to-day we haven't the heart to expel the painters and poets because we no longer admit to ourselves that there is any danger in keeping them in our midst."[4a]

In the last few years it must indeed have seemed that the main thing brought by painters and poets to society was danger. The most obvious characteristic of the inter-war culture was its destructiveness. At its simplest, this took the form of an emphasis on the base and ignoble results of our social existence. Whereas in the last century New England produced Emerson, with his rather pompous and provincial uplift, and Thoreau's back-to-Nature insistence on the simple virtues, in the 1920's it offered us instead T. S. Eliot's

> "For I have known them all already, known them all:
> Have known the evenings, mornings, afternoons,
> I have measured out my life with coffee spoons;[5]

and

> "The winter evening settles down
> With smell of steaks in passageways."[6]

and

> "When lovely woman stoops to folly and
> Paces about her room again, alone,
> She smoothes her hair with automatic hand,
> And puts a record on the gramophone."[7]

Another American, E. E. Cummings, lashed out around him with a less sure aim but getting more fun out of the slaughter and throwing in a bit of disruption of normal typography to add to the general hurly-burly:

> "i would
> suggest that certain ideas gestures
> rhymes, like Gillette Razor Blades
> having been used and reused
> to the mystical moment of dullness emphatically are
> No To Be Resharpened. (Case in point
>
> if we believe these gently O sweetly
> melancholy trillers amid the thrillers
> these crepuscular violinists among my and your
> skyscrapers—Helen & Cleopatra were Just Too Lovely,
> The Snail's On The Thorn enter Morn and God's
> In His andsoforth
>
> (do you get me?) according
> to such supposedly indigenous
> throstles Art is O World O Life
> a formula: example, Turn Your Shirttails Into
>
> Drawers and If It Isn't an Eastman It Isn't A
> Kodak therefore my friends let
> us now sing each and all fortissimo A——
> mer
> i
>
> ca, I
> love
> You. And there's a
> hun-dred-mil-lion-others, like

all of you successfully if
delicately gelded (or spaded)
gentlemen (and ladies)—pretty

littleliverpill—
hearted-Nujolneeding-There's-A-Reason
americans (who tensetendoned and with
upward vacant eyes, painfully
perpetually crouched, quivering, upon the
sternly allotted sandpile
—how silently
emit a tiny violetflavoured nuisance: Odor?

ono.
comes out lies a ribbon likes flat on the brush."[8]

This bawling-out of the universe, though it might be fun
while it lasted, could not of course get anyone anywhere.
Eliot, after a hard struggle, developed out of his original disillusionment into a profound poet, though one who relied
too much on the Church; but Cummings could only continue to develop his typographical extravagances into a sort
of word-making-and-word-taking game which is almost
completely incomprehensible except for a vaguely Fascist
flavour and occasional sparks of obscenity.

There were other artistic movements which seemed at first
to be just as purely destructive, but which have since turned
out to provide a basis for new types of constructive activity
which seem to lead somewhere. Just before the 1914 war,
some painters in Paris had started the cubist movement, which
began by analysing the painted representation of an object
into a set of simple intersecting planes. It was a highly technical affair, as incomprehensible to anyone but professional
painters as relativity mathematics is to the non-mathema-
tician; though since painters have to live by selling their
pictures to the public, there was a great pretence that everyone could follow what they were doing. The influence of
cubism on ordinary ways of thought was, in spite of its
technicality, as profound as that of the relativity theory.

Painters interested in cubism, and people who looked at cubist pictures or imitations of them, did not regard everyday objects in the everyday way, as things existing in a network of connections with other things, and associations with other ideas. A chair from the Cubist point of view was not something you sat on, and of a particular kind such as you are likely to find in a kitchen or a drawing-room or wherever it might be; it was just a thing of a definite shape, whose geometrical properties could be analysed, for purposes of putting it on to canvas, in a particular way, quite independently of people or rooms or anything else. Such a restricted and technical way of looking at things was soon carried to its limit and had to be amplified by adding something more interesting. Its importance was that it emphasised in painting the general scientific movement to analyse the world, concentrating on some aspects of it and leaving out the rest.

The part which it was generally agreed to leave out was the mass of hackneyed associations which Eliot, Cummings and the others fulminated against. But the poets were much less radical than the painters. Cummings's apparently hardboiled line gets pretty blurry when you follow it up. He attacked the sentimentality of other people merely in order to substitute his own: for instance,

> "touching you i say (it being Spring
> and night) 'let us go a very little beyond
> the last road—there's something to be found'

> "and smiling you answer everything
> turns into something else, and slips away . . .
> (these leaves are Thingish with moondrool
> and i'm ever so very little afraid)." [9]

And Eliot in his earlier and most influential poems put, in the place of the conventional ideas which he despised, a mixture of metaphors which emphasised the more depressing aspects of things, and associations with parts of culture which were too highbrow to have been contaminated by the common herd:

"The pain of living and the drug of dreams
Curl up the small soul in the window seat
Behind the *Encyclopædia Britannica*."[10]

The painters, on the other hand, analysed and dissected the objects they were supposed to be painting, and pared away the usual associations to such an extent that they found themselves with nothing left. Much of the writing by modern painters or their friends has been devoted to discussing what has happened to the objects which they used to portray. For instance, an article written just before the war by one of the best young English painters, John Piper, was called "Lost, A Valuable Object" and in it he said[11]: "The one thing neither of them (of the two kinds of painters he is discussing) would dream of painting is a tree standing in a field. For the tree standing in the field has practically no meaning at the moment for the painter. It is an ideal; not a reality." The artists of course regretted their inability to think of anything to paint. John Piper finishes his article thus: "It will be a good thing to get back to the tree in the field that everyone is working for. For it is certainly to be hoped that we shall get back to it as a fact, as a reality. As something more than an ideal."

Most painters have failed to find any real tree in the field. There are two different directions in which they looked for it. One group discovered that if one isolates an object completely from all its normal associations, a whole set of other associations, which are usually more or less buried and unconscious, tend to come to the surface of the mind, often bringing with them the peculiar emotional intensity which belongs to other unconscious manifestations such as dreams. The surrealists, or superrealists, set themselves to explore this new world of obscure symbolism which lies at the boundaries between normal existence and dreams or madness. They invented several techniques for getting themselves into the necessary state of mind; they went in for self-hypnotism or automatic writing or, more simply, relied on the surprising effect of bringing incongruous objects together in unlikely situations, as in one of their famous examples which spoke of an umbrella finding itself with a sewing machine on an operating table. Paul Nash[12] has explained the method of surrealism by referring to the poet André Breton, who said that "a statue in a street or some place where it would normally be found is just a statue, as it were, in its right mind; but a statue in a ditch or in the middle of a ploughed field is then an object in a state of surrealism. . . . It has, in fact, the quality of a dream image, when things are so often incongruous and slightly frightening in their relation to time or place."

The surrealists claimed that by showing that art was merely a question of getting into an unmatter-of-fact frame of mind, they had made it possible for everyone to be an artist. Everyone can dream and have irrational notions. When critics told them that they were merely playing with nonsense, they replied that the critics were being spiteful because the basis of professional criticism had been destroyed. Surrealism, said Max Ernst,[13] "has opened up a field of vision limited only by the mind's capacity for nervous excitement. It goes without saying that this has been a great blow to the critics, who are terrified to see the 'author's' importance being reduced to a minimum and the conception of talent abolished."

But what they had overlooked, of course, is that although everyone can dream and play the lunatic, very few people want to do so all the time. Surrealism has always been one of the standard brands of English humour; one finds it in ballads, in Shakespeare and in nonsense writers such as Lear; *Alice in Wonderland* is probably the best surrealist piece of literature so far. One of its most interesting present-day exponents is the American humorist Thurber. But these writers keep surrealism in its place. The modern group who call themselves Surrealists with a capital S fail because they try to use surrealism as a complete and satisfactory philosophy.

A new way of looking at the world which depends on

getting one's self to the borderline of madness is not a practical proposition as a general rule of life for the world at large. As a specialised activity carried on by a few people, it may produce some valuable new knowledge. In fact, in the more or less scientific hands of psychoanalysts it has certainly done so, and it is as an adjunct of this very important branch of scientific investigation that surrealism will develop in the future. As an influence on our general outlook on the world, the most that can be said for it is something else which Max Ernst also claimed: "We have no doubt that by yielding naturally to the business of subduing appearances and upsetting the relationships of 'realities' it is helping, with a smile on its lips, to hasten the general crisis of consciousness due in our time." But one would answer the smile with more cheerfulness if, instead of merely hastening the crisis, surrealism had been able to do something about solving it. As an attempt to find new objects worthy of the attention of a busy and intelligent world, it was too fairy-like to be a success.

The other main direction taken by modern painting, towards what is known as abstract art, has also failed to lead to a satisfactory "tree in the field." In fact, the painters who worked along this line have hardly as yet tried to come to terms with ordinary objects. They were interested in the relations between shapes and colours, in the effects which can be got by mere meaningless patterns and contrasts. This again is obviously a highly specialised and technical painter's affair, which one would at first sight think had nothing to do with ordinary life. But actually it has had a considerable amount to do with it. Abstract and formal pattern, of the kind the painters were interested in, is one of the commonest things in daily life, although one is usually hardly aware of it. Every manufactured article is made in some definite shape; chairs, typewriters, ashtrays are made in shapes suitable for the style of some particular age or way of life; the design of a page of newspaper, or the heading of a letter, reflects an attitude. And more than reflects it; these everyday appearances, that the user scarcely notices, but which somebody has thought out and put together, have a great effect on the people who handle them. Unconsciously their mind becomes attuned to a style, and something of the feeling of the designers gets across to the unwitting user.

The technical researches of the abstract artists, passing through the hands of the commercial designers, who somewhat messed them about, have undoubtedly had a great effect on the appearance of our man-made world.

It is very significant that nearly all the abstractionists were attracted to much the same kind of design. It was not flowery and ornamented, nor fluid and lyrical; it was a rather hard and severe art, sometimes clean and elegant, as in the pictures of Ben Nicholson and Helion, sometimes with Leger's rather brutal swagger, always depending on the subtle relations of simple things, circles, rectangles of different colours and textures, and firm, definite lines which might be drawn with a ruler or compass. The difference it made to everyday design is there for anyone to see in the coinage or postage stamps, particularly in the short-lived Edward VIII stamps, in which abstract simplicity was allowed to run away with itself.

Important as abstract painting has been as an influence on manufactured designs, it is not all that one could hope for as an art. Many of the artists themselves are not fully satisfied with it; as Piper pointed out in the quotation given above, one wants something more, one wants to get hold of real things again. An abstract picture is too indirect a way of approaching people; most spectators, unless they go in for that kind of thing, are conscious of getting from it only a very vague impression of a feeling, if that. But the difficulty is to put objects into paintings and keep the same freshness and freedom from moribund ideas, the same strength and clarity. When everyone is wondering just exactly where they stand, and just what things are important to them, what can the painter do with things except play the fool with them, like the surrealists; pretend it is still 1900, like the Royal Academy; or throw them out of the studio altogether like the abstractionists?

Circumstances conspired to force the artist to find an answer. It was not merely that the outbreak of the war showed the surrealists that lunacy (which they now saw all round them) is not enough, and exposed to the abstractionists the flimsiness of the vehicle in which they tried to convey their message. There were also potent bread-and-butter reasons bringing their painting to earth. Almost the only painters who were able to continue painting were those employed as war artists, recording the scenes of the strange world of war, or on the scheme for recording the monuments of England. Both these groups, in their official work, returned to representational painting; they were forced to look at trees in the field, and they had to discover how to do so. It was probably a good thing. Henry Moore's studies of coal-miners and of shelterers during the Blitz, Graham Sutherland's industrial scenes and sketches of burning towns, Piper's paintings of bombed ruins, and Paul Nash's of air fighting, were not only first-class art and first-class reporting; they also, if an outsider may hazard a guess, seem to have done these painters the valuable service of bringing them for a short time into inevadable contact with the major and obvious interests of their fellow men. It was a refreshing experience similar to that which the O.P.A. tried to provide for American artists in the middle 1930's, by setting the painters caught by the depression to doing "social" jobs, such as painting murals for public buildings. But the war was much more genuinely big stuff than were the social ideas behind the Rooseveltian New Deal; and the relation of the English artist to it was more spontaneous and direct than that of the American to the somewhat incoherent economic experiments of his President. And the best war art of England was certainly better than anything O.P.A. produced.

Moore, Sutherland, Piper and Nash, the four artists mentioned above, are typical of the present leaders of British painting. Although several of them have allowed themselves at various times to be called abstractionists or surrealists, none of them was ever fully assimilated into the conventional schools. They have all in different ways made an effort to rescue painting from being merely a highly technical branch of æsthetics, only comprehensible to the specialist, and have gone far to make it once again an important element in the main stream of civilisation.

There are of course a number of quite considerable artists who have, all through the period between the wars, stood apart from the general movements which have just been described. Men like Matisse, and Derain, and even more Bonnard and de Segonzac have been doing work which contains all the elements of a complete picture, and is not reduced to one aspect of it like an abstract or a surrealist picture. Their work has not been a cultural force of the same importance as that of the more extreme artists, simply because the world was not in a state in which complete pictures, or complete poems, were possible. The time was ripe for destruction and debunking, and one could not avoid the necessity for it by closing one's eyes. Among the really talented artists, almost the only ones who did not become surrealists or abstractionists were some of the older men. Standing aside from the main lines of thought, they could not develop their own work very much; to a great extent, each of them repeated his own line for years on end. But they could and did keep alive the belief that a picture could have a more direct relation to the everyday world, and express something as it were in ordinary language instead of in mathematical symbols. They were the people who kept the factory wheels turning between the decision to scrap the old model and the time when the new design was ready to go into production.

Almost the only man who took part in the changes which occurred in painting since World War I, but who could go on painting the natural things around him without repeating himself or anyone else, is Picasso, one of the inventors of cubism. He gets away with it by an intense interest in the world and in painting, which is so direct and personal that he seems to have no remembrance of the old ideas which the world is sick and tired of, and by an invention so fertile that there is no need to call in traditional ideas to help out. He has tried all the styles and invented many of them. He has been cubist, abstract and surrealist. He has played all sorts of tricks with the world, tricks which often depend basically on scientific ideas; for instance, his habit of painting faces which are both profiles and full-face views at the same time would hardly have occurred to any one before it became common knowledge that mathematics plays similar games with the co-ordinates of space and time. But he has never been content for long with pictures which are purely abstract or purely surrealist. He always comes back to painting the recognisable world, even if he does remodel it a good deal before he puts it down on canvas.

"To my misfortune," he says,[14] "and probably to my delight, I use things as my passions tell me to. What a miserable fate for a painter who adores blondes to have to stop himself putting them into a picture because they don't go with the basket of fruit! How awful for a painter who loathes apples to have to use them all the time because they go so nicely with the cloth! I put all the things I like into my pictures. So much the worse for the things—they just have to get on with it."

So he "distorts" things, as we say, to make them "go." And also to make them real. When Picasso paints a blonde, she is not like all the other blondes, Schoolgirl Complexion All Over, she is the genuine blonde article What Gentlemen Prefer. "Academic training in beauty is a sham. We have been deceived; but so well deceived that we can scarcely get back even a shadow of the truth. The beauties of the Parthenon, Venuses, Nymphs, Narcissi, are so many lies. Art is not the application of a canon of beauty but what the instinct and the brain can conceive beyond any canon. When we love a woman we don't start measuring her limbs." . . . "We have infected the pictures in museums with all our mistakes, all our stupidities, all our poverty of spirit. We have turned them into petty and ridiculous things. We have been tied up to a fiction, instead of trying to sense what inner life there was in the man who painted them. There ought to be an absolute dictatorship—a dictatorship of painters—a dictatorship of one painter—to suppress all those who have betrayed us, to suppress the tricksters, to suppress the means of betrayal, to suppress mannerisms, to suppress charm, to suppress history, to suppress a whole heap of other things. But common sense always gets away with it. Above all, let's have a revolution against that! The true dictator will always be got down by the dictatorship of common sense—and perhaps not."[14] But really yes. It is the dictatorship of the common sense of science which will get away with it; the common sense which is not afraid to acknowledge the rights of love, that peculiar commotion of the glands of internal secretion, but believes in measuring a woman's limbs before making her a present of a pair of slippers; which turns a table into a mathematical function much odder than anything the cubists ever drew.

For an intense and vivid life—which is what Picasso is preaching and what his paintings express—is not enough in itself if it has no intellectual and spiritual focus around which to concentrate, and no social background out of which to grow. And not even Picasso has been able to go far towards supplying them. The same failure is still obvious in the newest school of poets. Older people often complain that the second world war did not produce a crop of poets comparable to those of the first. The reason, surely, was that poets to-day are trying to tackle a more important and difficult task. The poems which became famous in 1914–1918 or just later were, after all, no more than fine expressions of rather immature thought—the adolescent and uncomprehending enthusiasm of Rupert Brooke or the cynical disillusionment of Siegfried Sassoon and E. E. Cummings. The best poets of that war, such as Wilfred Owen and Herbert Read, did not become known till much later. The recent war had been gathering for so long before it actually broke out on us, that all the early and easy reactions had been worked off on the Spanish episode—as thoroughly versified as anyone could wish for. When the major struggle started, poets knew that a major creative effort was demanded of them. It is significant that the main school which has, so far, emerged (and who call themselves rather grandiloquently the Apocalyptics), proclaim that their object is to teach men to "live more and exist less; it will be militant against all narrow, shallow half-thoughts and backdoor sniggerings". They welcome the "variety and multiplicity of life"; faith, enthusiasm, fertility are their watchwords. But this insistence on vigour and intensity, while salutary enough and an essential preliminary to any important advance in civilisation, is not yet canalised by any definite line of thought. It remains consciously and explicitly anarchic; and anarchism, attractive enough in its insistence on the value of the individual, remains always an emasculated movement because of its failure to recognise that man's individuality cannot be separated from the society in which he lives.

CHAPTER IV

ART LOOKS TO SCIENCE

WHOLEHEARTED destruction and tentative reconstruction; that is how one can sum up cultural activities between the two wars. What I want to argue in this chapter is that the paramount influence behind both these phases has been science. From being a matter of mundane "stinks," unworthy of the attention of the man of letters, of the scholar, of the philosopher, of all those whose business is to further the evolution of man's soul, scientific thought has become the pattern for the creative activity of our age, our only mode of transport through the rough seas in front of us.

I mean, of course, something much more important than a mere use by poets and painters of scientific subject matter. In poetry, in fact, there has not recently been any remarkable increase in the scientific metaphors or in the selection of scientific subjects. In the pioneering days of science in the seventeenth century, Donne made a fuller use of scientific notions than any important poet has attempted since.

> "As the tree's sap doth seeke the root below
> In winter, in my winter now I goe . . .

> "Eternall God, (for whom whoever dare
> Seeke new expressions, doe the Circle square) . . .

> "At the round earth's imagin'd corners, blow
> Your trumpets, Angells, . . .

> "But as in cutting up a man that's dead,
> The body will not last out, to have read
> On every part, and therefore men direct
> Their speech to parts, that are of most effect . . ."

Few poets at the present day seem to have attended anatomy

lectures, with demonstrations, or at least if they have they were not so impressed as Donne was.

The poets who have tried to use scientific imagery in recent times have often introduced it only in their more flippant works, such as Aldous Huxley's well-known *Fifth Philosopher's Song*, which begins:

> "A million million spermatozoa,
>   All of them alive:
>   Out of their cataclysm but one poor Noah
>   Dare hope to survive."[15]

or Auden's remark:

> "Are her fond responses
>   All-or-none reactions?"[16]

If they have been serious, the science has usually proved indigestible:

> "Courage. Weren't strips of heart culture seen
>   Of late mating two periodicities?
>   Could not Professor Charles Darwin
>   Graft annual upon perennial trees?"[17]

is not a very inspiring exhortation. It is obviously extremely difficult for the poet to decide just how scientifically sophisticated he can be. At one end of the scale one finds lines, like these from Empson's *High Dive*, which involve too specialised mathematics:

> "A cry, a greenish hollow undulation
>   Echoes slapping across the enclosed bathing-pool.
>   It is irrotational; one potential function
>   (Hollow, the cry of hounds) will give the rule."[18]

And at the other end, there is the too simple, such as this image from a poem by Spender describing two lovers who lie

> "Arm locked in arm, head against head
>   Whilst the nerves' implicit contacts
>   Through the hidden cables spark:"[19]

in which a somewhat crude reference to the physiology of nervous conduction merely suggests, to me at any rate, an incongruous picture of telephone connections in a hole in the street.

In fact, one would probably have to admit that if the poets are taken at their face value, there are at the present time a considerable number who have written apparently anti-scientific poems. Day Lewis, whose very colloquial idiom has enabled him to handle scientific ideas more adroitly than the authors mentioned above, is afraid that a scientific world would be rather nasty:

> "Pasteurize mother's milk
> Spoon out the waters of comfort in kilogrammes,
> Let love be clinic, let creation's pulse
> Keep Greenwich time, guard creature
> Against creator, and breed your supermen!
> But not from me."[20]

And in a poem in which the poet defends himself against various enemies, the third enemy is the pretentious scientific philosopher, who claims:

> "God is a proposition,
> And we that prove him are his priests, his chosen."[21]

But these are attacks on pseudo-science, on a doctrine which has forgotten the breadth of outlook and the humility in the face of facts which are an essential part of true science. They are poems which a scientist can enjoy and agree with; in fact, I shall in later chapters attempt to refute the same heresies myself, in a more pedestrian way. These poems which seem to be attacks on science are really defences of it; they use part of science's own resources to suppress its fifth column. That paradox explains why I feel justified in claiming John Crowe Ransom's *Persistent Explorer*[22] as one of my favourite scientific poems. Parts of it go as follows:

> "The noise of water teased his literal ears
> Which heard the distant drumming and thus scored:
> Water is falling—it fell—therefore it roared.
> But he cried, That is more than water I hear.

"But listen as he might, look fast or slow,
It was water, only water, tons of it
Dropping into the gorge, and every bit
Was water—the insipid chemical H_2O.

.   .   .   .   .   .

"The sound was tremendous, but it was no voice
That spoke to him. The spectacle was grand
But it spelled him nothing, nothing, and
Forbade him whether to cower or rejoice.

.   .   .   .   .   .

"But there were many ways of living too,
And let his enemies gibe, but let them say
That he would throw this continent away
And seek another country—as he would do."

A beautiful description of the formation of a scientific hypothesis, its experimental confirmation, and the refusal of the
scientist to accept that as the final end of everything he could
discover.

As far as subject matter goes, painters have on the whole
shown more sympathy for science than have poets. There are
many pictures whose whole subject matter is more or less
scientific. The dream images and unconscious associations
used by the surrealists of course existed before they were
scientifically studied, but it is only since psychologists became
interested in them that the world in general has been willing
to give them much attention, and it is doubtful whether surrealism would have been taken up as a "movement" in recent
years if Freud had not lived. "For we surrealists," says
Salvator Dali,[23] "as you will easily see if you pay us the
slightest attention, are not exactly artists and neither are we
exactly true men of science."

The subject matter of most abstract pictures is even more
clearly chosen from the objects well known to science. Some
artists, such as Ben Nicholson and Mondrian, use mainly the
simplest and most perfectly geometrical shapes, such as

circles, straight lines and rectangles. Others use more complex scientific concepts, such as series of lines which define a curve or a surface which is technically known as their envelope; one sees them in the paintings of Erni and some of the recent drawings and carvings of Barbara Hepworth. It is significant that the English abstract artists invited a scientist, Bernal, to contribute to their International Survey of Constructive Art, "Circle." He pointed out two further uses made by artists of scientific thought; the use of the more subtle relations of symmetry, and the use of irregular shapes which are not arbitrary but which are defined by some algebraic function, so that they might be a graph of some imperceptible physical quality, such as a distribution of electric charge.

These are some of the uses of science as subject matter by artists. It is in more fundamental respects that the influence of science has been really important. In the first place, the whole of what has been called above the destructive activity of the last twenty years was an essential prerequisite to the creation of a scientific style. Science is essentially analytical. It can look at any phenomenon, from something as cold and empty of significance as the orientation of a molecule on a surface, to the bearing of a man whose head is bloody but unbowed. But it must get its items separated; anything subjected to its scrutiny must be isolated from the mush of general goings-on in which it is normally embedded, it must be defined, or if it cannot be formally defined, at least one must be able to indicate what exactly is the thing one is talking about, and what else is the fortuitous rag-tag-and-bobtail that happens to be cluttering it up at the moment. And, after the twenty or thirty centuries of culture which we consciously inherit, everything was pretty completely mixed up with everything else. We had, as Picasso said, infected the pictures in our museums with all our stupidities, all our mistakes. Can anyone still hear God Save the King or the Star-Spangled Banner as a tune? Each is covered so deep with associations that our ears can hardly disentangle it. If a young man falls in love, the chances are that he finds his imagination cluttered up with a tedious rigmarole of roses and moonlight and so on. It was from science that the advice came to sort out the welter into its component parts; to separate the sexual physiology from the botany and meteorology.

Moreover the associations and prejudices which had clustered round each item of straightforward experience, and were smothering them as ivy smothers a tree, were derived from the old world which at the end of the first World War was already tottering under the impact of science, and must soon be altered out of all recognition by it. The focal points of our social life should have noble embodiments, said the pundits; a bank should be built in the classical style, a railway station perhaps in Gothic. But, answered commonsense, hacking away a few chunks of ivy, we are not living in the eighteenth century's imitation of classical Greece, nor do engine drivers necessarily aspire to reach Heaven by solitary contemplation and mortification of the flesh. Honour thy father and thy mother, said the fifth commandment; but scientific psychology showed that honour was hardly an adequate way of dealing with the complexities of family life. Love is a sacrament, the romantic poets cried; but science, leading off in the first round with that troublesome customer by cutting down most of the tree along with the ivy, said that love was a psychological corollary of a particular hormone balance, and Aldous Huxley's characters let it go at that.

> "Had they deceived us
> Or deceived themselves, the quiet-voiced elders,
> Bequeathing us merely a receipt for deceit?"[24]

asks Eliot in a poem published quite recently. The world was already saying "Yes" twenty years ago. And loud in the chorus was the voice of science.

If the old meanings clustering round our daily life were dead; if ancestral wisdom was a fraud or no longer applied;

if society was sick, and we had purged it to its bare bones,
where were we to turn for new values, fresh food to bring the
convalescent back to health? We have seen the surrealist
solution. Objects peeled of the coatings of emotion with
which generations of human experience have covered them
become ghosts of themselves, and can live a phantasmal life
hovering on the lunatic fringe of consciousness, producing in
men the vacuous mental excitement of paranoia. The only
other alternative to the grime of the outworn past is to consider things not as concretions of other men's thoughts and
feelings about them, but as agents which produce effects in
the world. To consider them, in fact, scientifically. If the
moon is a body giving off light of such and such a wavelength
and such and such an intensity, there is no smear of sentimentality over its face. Light of that colour and that bright-
ness can be significant and moving, not because we have been
told that the Moon is the Goddess of Love, but perhaps
because it abolishes differences of colour and fineness of
detail from what we see; or because we experience it at the
same time as silence and a relief from the necessity of doing
something soon; or even possibly for some more obscure
reason to do with the habits of life of our biological ancestors.

The scientific attitude to the world does not in the slightest
deny the emotional effects produced on men by their experience; what it tries to do is to classify the mechanisms by
which these effects were produced. Some will be more, some
less and some very little, dependent on associations inherited
from the culture of the past. If the more culturally dependent
are rejected, what is left is an immediate effect, directly
related to the circumstances of the actual experience, not
fictitiously heightened by a plausible reference to some
general but spurious theory. Consider, as an example of a
modern love lyric, a verse by Auden:[25]

> "Lay your sleeping head, my love,
> Human on my faithless arm;
> Time and fevers burn away

> Individual beauty from
> Thoughtful children, and the grave
> Proves the child ephemeral;
> But in my arms till break of day
> Let the living creature lie,
> Mortal, guilty, but to me
> The entirely beautiful."

In every phrase the poet is emphasising his refusal to consider the girl as anything but an ordinary girl, insisting on her normal humanity, and in the last line but one specifically rejecting, for himself, the concepts "mortal, guilty" with their theological connotations; but no one would claim that because of this matter-of-factness the poem is lacking in feeling.

A similar desire to discard the conventional ornaments, to get along without stage properties, can be seen in much of the best recent poetry of all the Western countries. Consider, for instance, this by Paul Eluard:

> On ne peut me connaître
> Mieux que tu me connais
>
> Tes yeux dans lesquels nous dormons
> Tous les deux
> On fait à mes lumières d'homme
> Un sort meilleur qu'aux nuits du monde
>
> Tes yeux dans lesquels je voyage
> Ont donné aux gestes des routes
> Un sens détaché de la terre
>
> Dans tes yeux ceux qui nous révèlent
> Notre solitude infinie
> Ne sont plus ce qu'ils croyaient être
>
> On ne peut te connaître
> Mieux que je te connais.

This attitude which I have called the scientific might be described in other ways. It is the matter-of-fact as against the romantic, the objective as against the subjective, the empirical, the unprejudiced, the *ad hoc* as against the *a priori*. The emotional tone which goes with it is quite definite and quite complex, although at first sight, and to those brought up in a different mode of thought, it may seem emotionless and banal, and although it does in fact reject the standard emotional responses which inherited culture have made the most automatic and obvious. But, as I said in an earlier chapter, this very rejection of inessential qualities, which now seem shoddy and superseded, is not an easy task. It demands a certain fervour, and it carries with it its own excitement, an excitement identical in kind with that of the scientist on the track of a new and relevant concept. And experiences stand out again bright and fresh and clean, like dolls which a child unwraps from a box of dirty cottonwool packing. Their corners are not rounded off by being seen through a fog of culture; each one has its full individual character as a part of the causal system of events which make up the world. At least that is what a scientific way of regarding experience would aim at, and when it is, rarely and with difficulty, fully attained, the achievement is no more "emotionless" than it must have been to Dalton when he reduced the untidy pile of facts about chemical composition to the law of constant proportions and the atomic theory; or to Mendel when he swept away a whole rubbish heap of nonsense about heredity and replaced it by his simple notion of the hereditary factor.

Definiteness and individuality of things, an interest in them as agents which produce effects, and an admiration of the elegance which results when the desired effect is exactly achieved with the minimum of fuss, these are the qualities of which science has in recent times been the main sponsor. It is because artists and writers since the last war have found in them the only way to advance that one is justified in saying that science is now in a position to become the leader of the humanities. Look at an abstract picture, by Leger or Nicholson or Mondrian; at the very first glance one is struck by the bright colours, the definite shapes and a controlled precision like that of a mathematical theorem. Even Picasso, with his much more total and less intellectual approach, writes that he sees things not as symbols, but with an almost innocent directness which would have been quite foreign to most periods of history but is not incongruous in our scientific age. "I paint a window just as I look out of a window. If a window looks wrong in a picture open, I draw the curtain and shut it, just as I would in my own room. One must act in painting, as in life, directly. . . . We must not discriminate between things. Where things are concerned, there are no class distinctions."[14] Again, listen to Eliot pointing out that the only way forward, even the only way to remain fully alive, is to deny the facile romantic ecstasy and to forget the traditional knowledge:

> "In order to arrive there,
> To arrive where you are, to get from where you are not,
>   You must go by a way wherein there is no ecstasy.
> In order to arrive at what you do not know
>   You must go by a way which is the way of ignorance."[26]

And the most considerable of the younger poets, Auden, has often expressed his debt to the scientific work of psychologists, as, for instance, in his fine poem in memory of Freud. In *Spain*, which dealt with the opening stages of the war, he describes the world as it should be after peace has been reached; and the main intellectual activity he mentions is scientific research:

> "To-morrow, perhaps, the future: the research on fatigue
> And the movements of packers; the gradual exploring of all the
>   Octaves of radiation;"[27]

The dedication of a recent book of his is a statement that the world is made hideous by baseless power, but can, and will, be saved by knowledge:

> "Every eye must weep alone
> Till I Will be overthrown.
>
> "But I Will can be removed,
> Not having sense enough
> To guard against I Know."

Of all the artists, it is perhaps the architects who have realised most fully both the scientific character of the point of view to which they have come, and the existence of an essentially poetic element in scientific thought. It is not difficult to see why; their field of activity is half scientific. Just as painters naturally associated with anatomists at the time when human bodies were first being systematically dissected and anatomy was made into a science, so architects, nowadays, confronted with new building materials such as glass and reinforced concrete, find it necessary to keep in touch with physicists and engineers. The usages of traditional building were suitable for materials like brick, stone and crude concrete, which will resist thrust or compression, but which are easily pulled apart by tension; wood was the strongest material at its disposal for holding tensions. The chief technical problems which fascinated the architects using those materials were the attempt to cover large areas with a single roof, without the need of supporting pillars, and the attempt to make a wall which was strong enough to support the roof and at the same time contained as large an area of transparent light as possible. Suddenly the modern architect is presented with materials, steel for taking tensions, reinforced concrete which takes both tensions and compressions, which enable him perfectly simply to roof far larger spaces than any of his ancestors could do with their most elaborate fan vaultings and domes, and completely to abolish the problem of the larger window, by making, if he wishes, the whole wall of glass. No wonder he must become an applied scientist to discover just what are the potentialities of his new materials.

Just as the architect's materials are new, so are many of his problems. Most of the large buildings which have been designed recently have been factories, hospitals, storehouses, etc., buildings whose uses are so definite that the architect must take them into consideration. He must know not only what will be done in the building, but how it will be done,

and why, so that he can think out the most convenient form
of building for that particular purpose. At every turn, the
materials he handles and the purposes he handles them for
force the architect into contact with scientific knowledge and
scientific ways of thinking.

Science influences architecture, as it does abstract painting,
not only in its materials but more profoundly, though perhaps
less directly, in its general outlook. Marcel Breuer, who in
his work makes very imaginative use of new materials (he
invented the steel furniture made from bent tubes) has said[28]:
"The basis of modern architecture, however, is not the new
materials, nor even the new form, but the new mentality; that
is to say, the view we take and the manner in which we judge
our needs. Thus modern architecture would exist even without reinforced concrete, plywood and linoleum. It would
exist even in stone, wood and brick." "The values (of the
new æsthetic)" says another architect, J. L. Martin,[29] "precision, economy, exact finish, are not merely the results of
technical limitation. They are the product of artistic selection." And the reason they are selected is that they fit in
with the scientific spirit, the adoption of which is the basic
revolution which has taken place in the world of architecture.
The attitude of the modern architect, who asks of a building,
say a railway station, What is it which goes on here? what is
my building required to do, and what will be the effects in
practical use of possible alternatives in design? is a fundamentally scientific attitude. It must have been a very subsidiary
and easily overlooked attitude among the classical architects
of the eighteenth century, for instance, who would often
make a lavatory as large as a bedroom for the sake of the
symmetry of their façade, or place the kitchen along with the
servants' quarters, and away from the dining room, so as to
express the cleavage between the upper and lower classes.
It is not yet the generally accepted attitude; banks prefer
looking respectable, disguised as Georgian houses, to experi-
menting to find the most convenient form, and the amount

of convenience which a dweller in the new suburbs will
sacrifice in order to look a little Tudor about the doorway,
Moorish in the gables, or Spanish Colonial in the veranda is
at first sight almost unbelievable.

The cultural basis of English suburbia has recently been
analysed in a very interesting book (*The Castles on the
Ground*) by J. M. Richards—a thoroughly educated modern
architect who feels sympathy with the tendencies he is discussing. Richards argues that one should look, not at
individual suburban houses, still less at details of them, but
at the suburban environment as a whole; and he says that if
we do so, we shall find that it has real value as a charming
world of fantasy, which the white collar office worker has
spontaneously created. It must not be judged, says Richards,
by the standards of the other two great classes of modern
man—the productive man interested in output, or the
consumer interested in quality: it is the world of the man
concerned with distribution. Which may be true enough as
far as it goes, but it does not go far enough. The suburban
ideal, as Richards admits, is one of escape, and no one can
be said to have mastered his position in life if his one desire
is to escape from it. Moreover it is not even an original
world of fantasy into which the suburban dweller escapes;
it is a ragbag of bits of the metropolis in the corner cinema,
and bits of the country in his lawns and shrubs; the turrets,
loggias and verandas with which his house is embellished
are reminiscences of all the architectural styles taught in the
local schools. If this is, indeed, as Richards claims, the
genuine people's art of to-day, we have to admit that we can
neither solve our problems nor think of anything new.

The most important point about architecture is that it is
in it, more than in any of the other arts, that the stupendous
practical effects of scientific and artistic theories become
most obvious. The modern architect must ask himself not
only how to build the most convenient factory; he must ask
himself how to house a man who wishes to live. Before he

can find the answer he must discover what goes on in a living-house; what is living, actually? It is no longer farming, as it was when the Tudor house was designed—they have become museum pieces: it is no longer the life of the bewigged and noble lords for whom the English Classicists built palaces—they have been turned into schools; it is no longer even the respectable bourgeois existence for which the Georgian terraces were built, with their servants' quarters in the attics and basements—they have been cut up into flats. The designers who try to set the stage for present-day life must attempt to discover its essential features; and by the setting they provide for it they will in their turn go far to determine its character.

Architects have found only two ways of approaching this problem. On the one hand they suggest some sort of rehash of the past; Academy Georgian, Tudor watered down with H. and C. in every bedroom, or a potpourri of all the past whose flavour is so faint that it may pass as inoffensive even when inflated to the size of a skyscraper. But this is clearly no solution at all, simply a shifting about from foot to foot before one decides in which direction the future lies. The alternative is to turn on man himself the same scientific scrutiny that the architect already uses on factories. And the most compelling characteristic of living in recent times, as opposed to the life of the recent past, is its scepticism, its abandonment of tradition, its devaluation of authority as such. It is the same characteristic as that which we have called the scientific attitude of the architect and artist; of course the same, since the architect also is a modern man, a contemporary of the advertisement copy-writer and the blacksmith out of work for the first time in six hundred years.

But the artist and the architect have a special responsibility. It is their duty to sum up and define a way of life. The lack of horses leaves the village blacksmith puzzled, and the advertisement writer has no time to determine whether there is anything which can be called truth. The architect who wished to build for a scientific and sceptical age had to, whether he liked or not, find out what was left when scepticism had done its worst.

The pundits would say that nothing was left; values, they said, are based on faith, or on ethical intuition or a whole host of other mysterious things, but at any rate not on science. Once call in question the accepted ideals, the ways of life and goals of striving sanctified by tradition, and there will be nothing to replace them; life will become empty and meaningless, and there will be no reason to prefer one setting for it to another. Nothing of the kind happened. The architects who considered human life from the sceptical scientific point of view were almost unanimous as to what things were valuable to it, and what kinds of houses would be good to build The only reason why anyone should be surprised at this is because the philosophers had nearly succeeded in making a corner in ethics, and persuading the rest of the world that they were the only people who knew what goodness really meant. But that is pure bluff. Goodness is a perfectly ordinary notion which comes into every field of experience, though things which are good in one field may be not so good in another, and one may be willing to leave the Absolute and Essential Good to the philosophers, since they, like everyone else, have never been able to get their hands on it. But obviously, in the world of typewriters, to take an example with which I am having some trouble at the moment, goodness means a high capacity for carrying out the functions proper to typewriters, namely making a certain set of symbols on paper. Every biologist who performs experiments with rats knows that a rat is an animal with certain behaviour and functions; a good rat is one in which those functions have been able to develop in their most definite and characteristic form, and conditions are good for rats in proportion as they allow this development to proceed completely and harmoniously, not inhibiting or exaggerating one part at the expense of another.

It may be objected that this is simply a commonsense view of goodness, and not in any way specifically scientific. But that is quite incorrect; it has only become a commonsense view recently, as the scientific habit of mind has become generally adopted. In the past, and in other societies, animals have been judged on quite other grounds, like the sacred cows of India. I do not know for what reasons people decided that black cats are good and bring luck. Nor do I know what was the ethical value of the horse, the noblest of man's helpers; nor just how wicked were the animals which were tried and executed for witchcraft in the Middle Ages; but I am sure that commonsense in those days was applying non-scientific criteria to things which we should now judge according to the outlook of science. If that outlook has become commonsense, that is all a scientist can ask for. But actually, although most people would be willing to admit that it is fairly good sense, it has not yet become common enough.

In the same way as the rat, man of to-day, even separated from his traditional culture, still appears to the scientific architect as a being with a certain character, requiring houses of a kind which will allow, in fact encourage, that character to express itself. Dig him out from under the thatched roof of a fake rusticity; disinter him from the palm-girt halls of the Hotel Splendide; search him out in a back room (with curtained-off kitchenette and bath) in a mansion built for a solid and fecund family in Maida Vale, release him from a row of back-to-backs in Shoreditch, and he will be found to be a creature who thrives in light and air, provided he gets the efficient heating and sanitation which modern engineering can provide; who would like to be tidy, but cannot manage it without help; who can enliven a simple wall with pictures to suit his taste, but merely shuts his mind when confronted with the perpetual frown of someone else's idea of a cornice. The man who has escaped from the mixture of rabbit warren and gin palace that we call a city is a definite enough sort of person. It is for him that the modern architect works.

It is this normal citizen that the architectural profession in England must satisfy in performing the largest demand which has ever been made on conscious intellectual town-planning—not only the remodelling of most of our big cities after their mauling from the air, but in addition the building of twenty new towns, not as haphazard growths, but as coherently thought-out communities fit for present day living, able to meet the competition of the traditional charm of the small country town. The prospects look good. Although in the big city architecture of office blocks and factories, America is far ahead of us, and in the design of individual modern houses we have probably no architects as good as the best Swedish, Swiss, French or American, when it comes to the laying out of a town which is neither a chaotic jumble nor an exercise in intellectual geometry, it seems quite likely that the young English town planners will not show up too badly on the world stage. Good town-planning, like gardening, is the art of making things grow naturally, healthily and in the right places; and gardening is something the English have always been good at.

CHAPTER V

SCIENCE'S FAILURE AND SUCCESS

ALL the cultural activities of our epoch have failed in their main function. Neither painting nor literature has been able to arrive at a point of view positive and definite enough to be worth even considering as a basis for a new society. They have been very useful; they have cleared away a lot of mess which everyone wanted to see the last of; they have indicated, rather hazily, the direction in which a new outlook on the world might be found; but they have not drawn the curtains and enabled us to look through on to a promised land.

Among the failures, one must also include science. In fact, its failure to realise and fulfil its social function is probably the most unfortunate of them all. It is, I have argued, actually the basis of the attitude to which the other cultural activities were trying to attain. The social consequences of the scientific habit of mind should have been a common topic of argument and criticism, a generally recognised subject for creative thinking, something of which first the leaders of contemporary culture, and then every educated person, would have heard and read and thought. Instead of that, the scientific world has often been, in its public and explicit expressions of opinion, unwilling to admit that its attitude has any relevance to social life, and it has hardly ever even dared to suggest that it has an important contribution to make.

It is only quite recently that the official leaders of science have begun timidly to approach the conclusion that science may have ethical consequences. Even now one gets the impression that the admission is made not so much from a firm intellectual conviction, but rather because the more generous spirits amongst them could not pass over the harnessing of science to war purposes without trying to find some mitigating prospect for the future. But at least it is significant and encouraging that both the last two Presidents of the Royal Society, Sir William Bragg and Sir Henry Dale, have publicly urged that scientists, because of their special knowledge, have special responsibilities. In America the problem was raised in a more urgent and less theoretical form, in connection with the atomic bomb. Who should decide whether it should be dropped on a living city? Who should decide whether it should continue to be kept secret? Normally the mechanism for the social regulation of enterprise is less developed in America than in Europe; it is the country of "individualism" which still regards socialism with the shocked and fearful horror we got over some fifty years ago. But one could hardly feel satisfied to hand the bomb over to the wisdom even of General Motors or Fords. It demanded control by the whole of society. The question was, who should represent society? Many of the scientists felt that, since they were the only people who understood the bomb, they should at least have a considerable say in deciding how to use it, and that their views on the ethical difficulties were to be taken seriously.

This was, however, only a partial realisation of the point I am trying to make, which is not only the (perfectly true) statement that for the solution of some ethical problems a detailed scientific knowledge is of the greatest value, but also that the general scientific method of dealing with situations should affect our whole thinking about social problems. And until the last year or two, even such partial admissions have been rare; when such matters are discussed at all, the authoritative announcements have usually been distressingly vague, a mere moaning for π in the sky. Poetry and the arts, in their tentative approaches to science before the war, were wooing a frigid adolescent.

There are several reasons for this: the first financial. Scientists, unlike artists and writers, do not earn their living in a free-lance, hand-to-mouth way, doing whatever interests them most provided they can pick up from somewhere enough to keep going. They hold definite salaried positions. Many of these positions are in industrial and manufacturing businesses, and are of course concerned with the particular activities of the firms who pay for them. The posts in Universities are less strictly tied to commercial interests, but even there the money has to be found from somewhere, and ultimately its source is in the business world which controls all large sums of money at the present time. The resources which a University has most fully under its control are usually earmarked for subjects which were of interest to the original donors of the funds many years ago, and the only place to find the means to support new work of another type is in the hands of other interests who hold the strings of a long purse. And the business world is not primarily interested in the investigation of social life, or in the formulation of what the scientific attitude has to contribute to it. Why should it be? Business men are caught up in a war to the death with their rivals, and what they want from scientific research is something which will help them to keep their heads above water—results which pay. Even if a successful man of affairs rises above the struggle and can indulge his fancy, his world is the world of production and manufacture, the sciences he is likely to be interested in are the technical ones, chemistry and physics and their newer offshoots. He is more likely to found a professorship in something like surface chemistry or crystal physics; perhaps only a retired advertising magnate would be expected to be primarily interested in social psychology.

In practice in England this financial starvation of the social aspects of science has been mitigated from only two sources. It turned out to be one of the minor blessings of an empire that it has natives in it, and that, in order to rule them satisfactorily, one has to know something about them. It is not too difficult to earn your living as a student of mankind provided you study the Bantu or the Melanesians or some other more or less primitive tribe; and the Briton irritated by American sneers about the Empire is sometimes tempted to retort that the only reason the settlers did not liquidate the entire indigenous population of North America was in order to leave some raw material for the anthropologists. This somewhat uncouth way of dealing with perhaps the most important problem of the time even has certain advantages. The social systems of the native races in our colonies are usually simpler than our own in many respects, and it would, perhaps, be easier for a scientist to analyse them first than to start straightaway on our own more familiar but less manageable way of life. But this is a theoretical point; on balance this approach to social problems is both trifling and beside the point. The study of native races is a small and not very impressive particular part of science, whereas the study of society as a whole should be one of its most active branches, attracting some of its best minds. Moreover the particular question which is of crucial importance at the present time, the effect of the scientific attitude on social aims and structure, cannot by the nature of things be studied in the wilds of Africa, where the sociologist is probably the only particle of science in sight.

The main other sources of supply for the English student of society have been some of the great American research foundations, particularly the Rockefeller Foundation. The whole of the American way of life has been built up in a more or less uninhabited wilderness within the last four hundred years, and there has been scarcely any time during that period at which some part of the country was not beginning from scratch to form itself from a collection of isolated pioneers into a community. It is no wonder that Americans are more interested in the processes of social change than are Europeans, the inheritors of a centuries-long tradition of culture. Thus we find the president of the Rockefeller Foundation in 1939 writing as follows, and not only writing but implementing his words to the comforting tune of two million dollars: [30]

"Democracy to-day needs the social scientists, both inside and outside the universities. It needs to free them to think with all possible penetration, wherever that thinking may lead. New ideas about human relations and institutional adjustment should be fully, honestly and hospitably analysed. Society should be most deeply concerned not with ridiculing failures or condemning those whose findings it does not approve, but with aiding that small minority of pioneers whose work in the social studies is reaching up to new levels of scientific achievement. Such persons are to be found in universities, in government and in private life. No greater contribution to the disinterested comprehension of to-day's issues could be made than by affording these able men and women full opportunity to make their work genuinely effective."

This paragraph puts its finger on some of the other influences which have kept science in general and social science in particular from having its full effect on human affairs. Ridiculing failures and condemning those whose findings it does not approve are pastimes which society has been only too fond of; and scientists themselves are not guiltless of sometimes joining in. Often the pressure is a direct reactionary one in the ordinary political sense. It is clear that there are a great many inefficiences and failures in our economic system which are kept in being because they are to the advantage of powerful interests; and those interests are not going to be pleased with a scientist who points them out. Social science, in fact, is a dangerous profession; if you are tactful enough not to offend the mighty, you are not likely to be interesting enough to cut much ice. And if the scientist himself did not realise it, the officials to whom he owed his appointment certainly did. "Our university administrators," says Professor Lynd of Princeton,[31] "are concerned in their enforced daily decisions with the short-run welfare of an institution, and this may not be viewed as synonymous with the long-run welfare of our American culture. To go ahead frankly into the enlarged opportunity confronting the social sciences invites trouble. Putting one's head into the lion's mouth to operate on a sore tooth has its manifest disadvantages."

The situation would have been much easier if the sociologists had been able to count on the respect and support of other scientists, but they usually could not. Science, at the time when organised religion was its enemy, had signed away its rights to have views on the most general questions in return for freedom to put off its swaddling clothes. The older humanities, philosophy, classics, literature, felt that the bargain should still be kept, and many scientists, brought up on the basis of that arrangement, agreed with them. The point of view was particularly clearly put by the physiologist, Professor A. V. Hill,[32] in 1933 (it is not necessarily his view now; the fact that in 1939 he entered Parliament as Member for Cambridge University suggests that he has changed his mind).

"If scientific people are to be accorded the privilege of immunity and tolerance by civilised societies, however, they must observe the rules. These rules could not be better summarised than they were 270 years ago by Robert Hooke. . . . 'The business and design of the Royal Society is—To improve the knowledge of natural things, and all useful Arts, Manufactures, Mechanick practises, Engynes and Inventions by Experiments—(not meddling with Divinity, Metaphysicks, Moralls, Politicks, Grammar, Rhetorick or Logick)'; . . . Not meddling with morals and politics; such, I would urge, is the normal condition of tolerance and immunity for scientific pursuits in a civilised State . . . science should remain aloof and detached, not from any sense of superiority, not from any indifference to the common welfare, but as a condition of complete intellectual honesty."

Perhaps scientists would be happier if it could be so; but it is an impossible dream. Hooke's list makes pathetic reading. Divinity, Metaphysicks, Moralls, Politicks, Grammar,

Rhetorick, Logick—science has meddled with them as gently as a bomber raid with an ammunition dump. Hardly one concept of any of these subjects has survived intact from Hooke's day to this, and science has been one of the main causes of their transmutation. Its influence on such general topics cannot be avoided; so surely it might as well be open, and subject to debate and criticism by scientists themselves as well as by those who only know the subject at second hand. If tolerance is all that we hope for, a civilised society will tolerate opinions on matters of importance and not only on those which are too technical for it to understand.

But there is no doubt that among scientists themselves the social sciences were, at least in England, though less so in America, considered not quite respectable. There are of course more solid grounds for that view than mere timidity. Man's social behaviour is an activity of the sort with which science has always found most difficult to study. It cannot be simply analysed into component parts, so that one distinguishes clearly, for instance, between economics and politics, or between either of these and traditional custom. A society is in some ways a unity, and all its different aspects overlap on to one another, so that it is extremely difficult to draw any valid conclusions about any one part without studying them all. Somewhere, one feels, there should be a clue as to what it is which holds together all the diverse facets of a culture, its religion and its games, its business morals and its sense of individual worth, its economic structure and its sexual ethics. The standard scientific methods of dealing with things were worked out for simpler situations, and when applied to objects which are both complicated and highly organised and unified, they tend to yield a lot of isolated facts about details but to let slip the secret of the thing as a whole, which is what one is after. It is an orthodox and respectable scientific technique to measure things, if necessary to measure two or more things, and find how well the measurements fit. Sociologists did so in a big way, determining how the marriage rate varied with the wholesale cost of manufactured or agricultural products, or how the proportion of a wage spent on rent varies with the amount of wage received and so on. Very interesting many of these facts are; but they should be the mere foundation of a science; they are "data," things given, but not things which have been received and used and turned into something by the creative imagination.

As one of the most prominent American sociologists put it:[33]

"We social scientists have great arrays of data;

". . . data on production and distribution, but not the data which will enable us to say with assurance, as the experts dealing with such matters, how our economy can get into use all of the needed goods we are physically capable of producing:

". . . data on past business cycles, but not the data that enabled us to foresee the great depression of 1929 even six months before it occurred:

". . . data on labour problems, but not the data to provide an effective programme for solving the central problems of unemployment and of the widening class-cleavage between capital and labour:

". . . legal data, but not the data to implement us to curb admittedly increasing lawlessness:

". . . data on public administration, but not the data for a well co-ordinated programme with which to attack such central problems of American democracy as the fading meaning of 'citizenship' to the urban dweller and what Secretary Wallace has called the 'private ownership of government' by business:

". . . data on the irrationality of human behaviour and on the wide inequalities in intelligence, but not the data on how a culture can be made to operate democratically by and for such human components."

If this was the state in America, English science was certainly no better off. In fact, being further away from the sources of financial support provided by the American research foundations, even its collections of data on social questions were much less complete. Above all, they were even less related to the living reality of life in our civilisation.

We had our censuses and economic statistics, less exhaustive than the American but still fairly thorough. But there was on this side of the Atlantic very little to correspond to the enormous mass of American data on questions of personal taste and interest, on such matters as the relation between a husband's profession and his views on whether a woman's place is the home, or on the kinds of activities with which the unemployed tried to occupy themselves during their enforced leisure.

Something was done to improve things during the war. The Wartime Social Survey was set up, and, having dropped the "Wartime" from its title, still keeps going. Its activities had one great practical advantage over those of most of the American investigations; they were intended to provide data for immediate use in dealing with problems of major importance to society, matters such as reactions to being bombed, attitudes to food rationing and so on. Most previous social surveys had either been, as Lynd suggests, rather pointless exercises, or were related to the comparatively narrow interests of particular sales or advertising organisations. Quite recently the technique of social surveying began to be used in intimate contact with the widest possible projects of social creation. It is becoming recognised as an integral part, just as important as the mapping of physical resources, in the planning of new towns or the replanning of old ones. For instance, in Max Lock's plan of Middlesbrough, the grouping of the new town into units, the provision of schools, shopping centres and so on, was based on a study of what in fact are the effective neighbourhood units at present, for which activities people remained in their neighbourhood, for which they went outside it and so on.[34]

Such work establishes an almost ideal set-up for one end of the spectrum of scientific research, namely its connection with practice. But social science will only prosper if the other, more abstract, end is also adequately catered for. The practical work is bound to throw up problems (the nature of the cohesion of social groups, for instance) which will demand special experimental studies of no immediate practical application. Such work is bound to be costly. There are still very few people engaged in it; and it is difficult to believe there will be many more until a more satisfactory method of financing it is found.

Descriptive surveys of human behaviour, important and worthy enterprises though they may be, are not by themselves enough to furnish a full understanding of our civilisation. A society is an organised whole, and cannot be completely comprehended by the mere collection of facts about it. The task is one which demands that peculiar quality which we call imagination or intuition or insight; and the first imaginative attempts to break the complex down into elements which have some importance are likely to produce ideas which have a somewhat cranky, half-baked look. The language in which they are expressed is usually uncouth and full of newly invented jargon, feeling after the new ideas which the author cannot yet put down simply but must try to convey by implication rather than by precise definition. Older sciences which are pushing ahead from a well secured base at the end of a long and well charted road of previous discoveries may well be tempted to look down their noses at such guerilla parties. But the skirmishers are out on the track of social order, and they will get a satisfactory analysis for it in time. The most promising of the purely scientific attacks is coming from the anthropologists. Malinowski showed how the behaviour of some tribes hung together as a system functioning to keep them alive and their society in being. The Americans Benedict and Mead, and the Englishman Bateson, have widened the analysis to include not only physical behaviour but also the intellectual system of beliefs and theories, and the set of emotional attitudes and feelings which are part of life in the group.

We could have made good use of such ideas in relation to

our own society in its present state of disintegration and change if they had been more fully developed. But they have not been; and the last of the reasons one may mention for this comparative neglect is the parallel, within science, of the very disintegration of society which social science might have enabled us to overcome. For as our civilisation has lost its unity and become a collection of individuals with innumerable different sets of beliefs and ideals, science in general has tended to become an enormous collection of details. Again, there is a certain degree of justification for this. Scientific knowledge and understanding is a communal achievement, the sum of a multitude of contributions from many different people. Any individual may feel a certain justifiable pride if he knows that he has added one brick to the structure. But in recent years, more I think than in the past, it has been commonly assumed that the discovery of one or two nuggets of knowledge is all that a scientist need attempt. So long as his facts are correct, and his hypothesis within its narrow limits does not lead to any contradictions, his duty was thought to be done. Any attempt to take a broader view of a complex problem as a whole, and to assess the importance of the various elements in it, seemed inappropriate in an age when there were few generally accepted views about major problems in any field of activity. It was orthodox and acceptable to discuss the relation between two or possibly three of the individual concepts of science, but anything more comprehensive than this tended to be thought slightly disreputable, mere speculation or word spinning.

In the words of the old cliché, in fact, scientists have tended to refuse to see the wood for the trees. There have been an army of bricklayers piling brick on brick, even plumbers setting up super W.C.'s, and heating and lighting engineers installing the most modern equipment; but they have all united to shoo the architect off the building site, and the edifice of knowledge is growing like a factory with a furnace too big for its boilers, its precision tools installed in a room with no lighting, and anyhow with no one who knows what it is supposed to manufacture.

Just as the character of the typical modern man became so disorganised that he could no longer be described by some adjective such as Quaker or Liberal or Catholic, which applied to all aspects of him, but had to be called something like insurance agent or business executive, which leaves most of his character out of the picture; so the ideal of the scientific world ceased to be the man of science as a complete and adult man all of whose activities were permeated with the scientific attitude of mind, and became the specialist, the veterinary helminthologist, say, who knew all about one or two families of parasitic worms, but kept this knowledge quite separate from anything else that he might happen to be interested in. To give a scientific opinion meant to expound the consequences of some specialised field of knowledge. Responsible scientists, looking at their colleagues, saw the obvious fact that most specialists were quite unfitted to play an important part in the evolution of general culture; but far from acknowledging that this was a sign of science's failure, they accepted it almost with glee as an excuse which let them out of the necessity of thinking about wider issues. It tended to be forgotten that there are certain general characteristics of scientific knowledge as a whole, and that where the specialised field has been inadequately developed, as in the social sciences, there may still be some opinions which follow logically and necessarily from these fundamental features common to all scientific thought.

Here is a very pretty example of the current confusion between the two kinds of scientist, the technical expert and the man who thinks scientifically. One of the four or five most influential scientists in England recently wrote[35] in praise of a young American physicist who said to him "If I want to express opinions on morals or politics I do so as a citizen, not as a scientist." That is reasonable enough if scientist means technical expert, since very few scientists are experts on wage rates, rearmament policies, etc. The plausibility of the sentence when interpreted in this trivial sense undoubtedly tempts one to believe that it is also true when "scientist" is given its full, wide meaning. The recommendation is then, put bluntly, that when considering morals or politics one should discard the scientific habits of thought; the search for unbiassed evidence, the checking of theory by practice, the interest in causal relations and the lack of interest in things for their own sakes. It is advice that very few scientists are likely to admit to following, if it is put squarely and unambiguously before them. The trouble is that it usually is not presented clearly, but, as in this case, is cloaked in all kinds of ambiguities and half-truths, which make it easy to slink round the corner murmuring "It has nothing to do with me." Even the author who quoted it probably did not really mean it; at least he used it, not as one would expect, against people who allowed their science to influence their politics, but against those whose politics had in his opinion influenced their science, which is quite another story; and he is himself justly respected as one of the most active and conscientious scientists concerned with public affairs. At any rate, whichever of these senses the physicist's dictum is supposed to have, they all agree in stating that science has nothing to do with politics or morals; and you can interpret *that* in several different ways, but there is one way at least, and that the most important, in which, as I have argued above, it is quite untrue.

In spite of this failure to realise that the scientific attitude has social implications, and in spite of the lack of development of the sciences which should deal with man's social behaviour, science has been a very potent cultural force. Its success within its own field has ensured that much, in a period when other branches of culture have produced very little whose value they can be certain of. What poets or artists or philosophers are there to match against the great scientists whose work has become of importance since the last war;

Einstein, Rutherford, Bohr, Planck, Freud, Morgan and the rest? Some of their work may have been done before 1914, but it was in the between-wars period that it enlarged our basic ideas of the nature of space and time, of the material the world is made of, of how our minds work, and of the fundamental nature of living things. This was not an achievement of a few isolated men of genius; in all these subjects the enormous advances in knowledge and understanding were aided by the efforts of a large number of people, some good, some not so good, but all together turning out a volume of radical but inescapable stuff with which the other cultural activities cannot begin to compete. No wonder poets and artists began to suck in a little scientific vapour with the air they breathed.

CHAPTER VI

THE EMPTINESS OF FASCISM

For the first ten or so years after the first World War, the development of cultural activities in Germany was very similar to that in England and France. There was the same destruction and breaking down of accepted beliefs and customs, and the same attempts to build, from a scientific basis, something new to put in their place. The main difference was that in Germany both movements were more violent. The war did not cease for the Germans at the Armistice in 1918; the blockade against them was enforced for nearly a year longer, and there was fighting going on in Poland, Silesia and the Baltic countries for some time. Part of their country was occupied, and their economic system blew up into fragments in the great inflation which destroyed the whole structure of their society. No wonder that, even more than in other countries, people felt that they had no secure position in life, that all their preconceived beliefs and traditional values had failed them and must be got rid of; that liberty, equality and fraternity were moonshine; faith, hope and charity ended in the gutter; and even money didn't mean anything for more than a few days or hours at a time.

So their artists and writers were more virulently and crassly destructive than those in any other country. No pictures have ever been aimed at all previous ideas of beauty with more sardonic hate than the Merzbilde of Kurt Schwitters, made as mosaics by gumming together bits of dirty newspaper, bus tickets and so on. It would be difficult to find caricatures more devastating, and less relieved by humour, than the drawings of Georg Grosz. One of the great popular successes of about 1930, and a considerable work of art as well, was the "Three Ha'penny Opera," modelled to some extent on our Beggar's Opera, but placed in a modern setting. Its pessimism was extreme and very complex. The highwaymen and their girls were transformed into a sort of fifth column of the ill-used; with all the cruelty, as well as the pity, that that implies; definitely "on our side," but equally definitely knowing that they would be defeated.

What love poem could be more flat and hopeless than this by Kastner:[36]

> "Du zürntest manchmal über meine Kühle.
> Ich muss dir sagen: Damals warst Du klug.
> Ich hatte stets die nämlichen Gefühle.
> Sie waren aber niemals stark genug.
>
> ("You blazed up sometimes about my coolness.
> I can tell you: You had something there.
> I always had the relevant emotions.
> But never enough to turn a hair.")

On a higher plane, there was the surprising popularity of the poet Rilke. A great poet, too difficult to be widely read in ordinary times; but he expressed a pessimistic mysticism which suited the feeling of that time; for instance, in the lines: [37]

> "Dir schien,
> weil du gewohnt warst an die andern Masse,
> es wäre nur für eine Weile; aber
> nun warst du in der Zeit, und Zeit ist lang.
> Und Zeit geht hin, und Zeit nimmt zu, und Zeit
> ist wie der Rückfall einer langen Krankheit.
>
> ("You thought,
> because you were used to another standard,
> it was only for a while; but now
> you were caught in Time, and Time is long.
> And Time goes on, and Time mounts up, and Time
> is like the relapse of a long illness.")

There were also German movements which began to work out a new conception of life which would have its own values and could provide something by which a man could find life worth living. They accepted the work of the cultural demolition squads, and also tried to build something new on the cleared ground. They were daring and thorough, and in their time were in the very forefront of all the European groups which were trying to lay down the lines along which a new society could be formed. The most famous of the German groups, and the most influential, was known as the Bauhaus, or building-school (now enjoying a second lease of life in Chicago). For it was again the architects who, because their artistic creation is most nearly in contact with the lives of ordinary people, had been forced both to accept the fact that the traditional ways of life had led to disaster and to find some point of view which would provide a setting for the life which continued. The attitude with which they approached their work was very clearly the parallel, in the artistic field, of the mental attitude of the scientist in his field. Instead of dealing with things as objects full of meanings which have been given them by people in the past, and have been handed on to us by tradition, they looked at them with fresh eyes, neglecting their coating of acquired meanings, but analysing them for artistic purposes into their basic colours, textures and patterns. With these elements they started to make their new works of art.

They worked consciously for a scientific age, an age of mass production and machine finishes. The most important, or at least the most influential part of their output did not consist of pictures or works of art in the conventional sense, but of designs for things of practical use, crockery, saucepans, furniture, books, posters and so on. Their products were taken up and mass produced by German firms, and the style of their designs spread from there over the whole world. A very great deal of the more up to date parts of our surroundings look the way they do because of the work of the Bauhaus. The simple spherical hanging electric light fittings, wall papers which have a texture but no definite pattern, steel furniture, ouilt-in cupboards, are some examples of things which they either invented or first popularised. If the objects among which a man spends his life have any influence on his outlook and feelings, the group of men who worked at the Bauhaus are some of the most important artists there have been since the last war.

But they lost in their own country and they have not yet won anywhere. The new way of life which they were pioneering was too slow in coming. The old German culture had been a rather tightly organised one; people knew their place and what was expected of them, and they had only to behave themselves to be free to drink their beer and listen to their concerts and operas and enjoy themselves. The disintegration of society and the disappearance of all generally accepted rules of what was fitting and right, were probably harder for the Germans to bear than for any other nation of Europe; they were brought up to do their recognised duty and they could not bear the effort of thinking out for themselves what it was. When the great depression of the 1930's came, their civilisation was more completely disorganised and out of gear than anyone else's. There are good pictures of it in the novels of the time, Kästner's *Fabian* and Döblin's *Berlin Alexanderplatz*, for instance. The whole place was chaos; and people were ready to accept any cure so long as it came quickly.

The reasons why it was the Nazi cure which was accepted were of course complex, as reasons always are in social affairs. One of the main causes was that in Germany, as in the rest of the world to this day, the forces which were defining a new outlook of a scientific type had failed to realise their unity and had been unable to get themselves across to people with sufficient clarity and explicitness to constitute a strong volume of powerfully held belief. In particular, the scientists had as a whole stood apart from the general cultural movement which was ultimately based on their unconscious influence. They carried on with the lazy, timid belief that science is concerned with a variety of out of the way phenomena among electrons and insects, but not with the daily life of man; and they still had the dangerous illusion that the other side made the same mistake. Then the leaders of the political parties who could most easily have adopted the scientific attitude, the Social Democrats and Communists, were undecided and weak, while their opponents, who stood for beliefs incompatible with science, were ruthless and daring, and reaped the advantages of money (not that money was a very definite thing in post-inflation Germany) and a tradition of ruling (which should have counted for nothing at a time when all traditions were garbled).

The reactionary political forces would have been comparatively powerless if they had not been able to find some other system of thought, which equally with the scientific was a break with the past, and which could be pushed as an alternative way out of Germany's confusion. Such an alternative existed in Germany much more strongly than in any other European countries, in the form of the youth movements. It was a mixture of the ideas which were running through these movements with old-fashioned nationalism and militarism which produced the witches' brew of Hitlerism, and it was the elements derived from the youth movements which gave the real kick to it.

The influence of these pre-Hitlerian youth movements is too often forgotten at the present time, but I believe it is impossible to understand the peculiar nature of the Nazi system of beliefs without remembering them. They were groups of young men, and sometimes women, who went in for hiking, camping and sports generally, rather like boy scouts. But they were young people profoundly disillusioned with the world, and the knots they played with were tied not in string but in their own personalities. They rejected the squalid inflation-world they lived in and went out into the woods to look for something else. They were young and inexperienced. They found nothing of what they were looking for; nothing at all; but they made do with that.

It is the fundamental fact about Nazism that at the basis of it, where there should be the foundations on which the whole structure of beliefs rests, there is nothing at all. It is just talking to keep one's courage up, holding one's self up by one's socks. The sort of thing the youth movements came back from the woods talking about was, to quote one of their few English representatives, "a night-time religion—that elemental unreason from which wisdom is absorbed as nurture is sucked by a tree-root from the soil." That was the kind of wind in the trees which gave these empty young men the illusion that they had filled their bellies with solid meat.

Nazi intellectuals were later to write almost exactly the same kind of nonsense and describe it as the basis of their whole outlook. [38] "Blood and soil, as the fundamental forces of life, are, however, the symbols of the national-political point of view and of the heroic style of life. By them the ground is prepared for a new form of education. . . . What does blood mean to us? We cannot rest satisfied with the teachings of physics, chemistry or medicine. From the earliest dawn of the race, this blood, this shadowy stream of life, has had a symbolic significance and leads us into the realm of metaphysics. Blood is the builder of the body, and also the source of the spirit of the race. In blood lurks our ancestral inheritance, in blood is embodied the race, from blood arise the character and destiny of man; blood is to man the hidden undercurrent, the symbol of the current of life from which man can arise and ascend to the regions of light, of spirit and of knowledge."

Nothing but words, chatter. The author does not mean blood in the ordinary sense; he specifically rejects the ordinary means of knowledge about it, and he probably knows as well as anyone that our ancestral inheritance is no more, and no less, in our blood than in our kidneys, that our character arises from our blood much less than from our pituitary glands. Blood is just an emotional word to him; it doesn't mean anything, but it makes you feel good.

But words are powerful things. The irrational nonsense turned out by Rosenberg and the other Nazi theorists did produce a comfortable feeling in many puzzled and unhappy Germans. It was so sweet a jam, and was pushed down their throats with such persistence, that they swallowed the most amazingly unpleasant pills along with it. They would not have taken it, probably, if there had not been very powerful groups forcing it on them. But similarly the big industrialists and bankers who provided Hitler's war chest could not have steered the development of society in the way they wanted it to go if they had not been able to find some fundamental attitude which they could use as a vehicle to put over their programme.

Money power cannot bring about changes in social structure directly; it must find some method of translating itself into emotional attitudes and intellectual values. The importance of this step is obvious from a comparison of Germany with Spain; Hitler, who made a psychological attack, entirely destroyed the most powerful labour movement in Europe with very little bloodshed, and not only enslaved the workers in his machine, but persuaded the majority of them to like it, while Franco and his allies, making a direct military attack with no preliminary psychological groundbait, were held at bay for two years by a completely new and only half organised democracy, and finally achieved a much less complete victory. The purely economic explanations of Hitlerism, which go no further than to classify it as a form of monopoly capitalism, are unduly simplified. They are dangerous because they obscure the fact that the stage of translating power into socially effective dogma is one of the few occasions when the privileged few have to descend to much the same level as everybody else, and can be met on more or less equal terms. They may still have some advantage in the means of propaganda at their disposal, but the goods they have to sell are so much less inherently attractive to the prospective

purchasers that they should be in the position of needing all
the help they can get and then some more.

All the other fascist philosophies have the same fundamental baselessness as the Nazi system. If one digs down to
the buried chest where they keep their ultimate beliefs, and
looks inside it, one feels like a liaison between Mr. Jorrocks
and Old Mother Hubbard; it is hellish dark and smells of
cheese, and empty at that. Italian Fascism, according to
Mussolini, [39] "conceives of life as a struggle, considering that
it behoves man to conquer for himself that life truly worthy
of him." But if one asks what is the life truly worthy of man,
one does not get much help. "The world seen through
Fascism is not this material world which appears on the
surface, in which man is an individual separated from all
others and standing by himself, and in which he is governed
by a natural law that makes him instinctively live a life of
selfish and momentary pleasure. The man of Fascism is an
individual who is nation and fatherland, which is a moral
law, binding together individuals and the generations into a
tradition and a mission, suppressing the instinct for a life
enclosed within the brief round of pleasure in order to restore
within duty a higher life free from the limits of time and
space; a life in which the individual, through the denial of
himself, through the sacrifice of his own private interests,
through death itself, realizes that completely spiritual
existence in which his value as a man lies."

Which means, so far as I can see, no more than that man
is naturally bad, on the material plane, but can become
spiritually valuable if he does his duty. But again, duty to
what? Presumably to Mussolini, as no higher authority is
specified. The appeal to spirituality means exactly nothing
except a command to the Fascist to be obedient.

The Nazi theories did not remain a mere bundle of nonsense. In the first place, they achieved what the German
people were asking for. They produced a coherent society;
not one, perhaps, in which the average German was very

happy, but at least one which could be understood, which had a fairly definite character and aims; a society in which, if one went with the stream, one did not need to feel lost, at any rate for a time. And, secondly, although the foundations of the society were profoundly irrational, there was no need for all the superstructure to be so too. There were many Nazi arguments, subsidiary to its main theory but still important enough, which were perfectly sensible and probably true, at least in their negative aspects: for instance, their criticism of the structure of Europe, that a hotchpotch of small independent nations is simply not feasible in the space at the present date in history, with a technical civilisation as highly developed as ours.

Again, in some technical spheres, Germany under the Nazis showed the same bold competence which always has been one of her characteristics. Pre-Nazi Germany had done some very fine work in building housing schemes and garden suburbs; although the Nazis cut down on this, they kept some of the projects going, and managed to persuade many people that they were responsible for the rest, which was quite untrue. But in subjects which fitted in with their social programme, they have often really been strikingly efficient. For instance, some of their aeroplane hangars are extremely beautiful buildings, making the most daring and successful use of new materials like shell-concrete in a way which gives a thrill to anyone interested in technical achievements. The great auto-roads, with their viaducts, bridges, and underpasses, were wonderful feats of engineering, flowing across the countryside with a magnificence and sweep which can leave no one unmoved. Germans, seeing these things and being proud of them, felt that the régime which produces them must be worth something. It is difficult to remember always that technical efficiency is not enough by itself, and that it can be used just as well or better to give man a richer and fuller life as for purposes which ultimately neglect his welfare and serve only the glory of the State.

The excellence of some of their technique cannot obscure the fundamental opposition between the Nazi ideas and the scientific attitude to society. One of the great slogans of the early days of the Nazi revolution was "Gemeinnutz vor Eigennutz," commonwealth before private wealth. It sounds like a statement which science might make, that in judging whether a thing was good for society, one has to consider whether it is good for the whole society and not for just a few individuals. But the Nazis shifted its meaning ever so slightly, and turned it thereby into a totally unscientific notion. What they meant by commonwealth was not the actual good of all the members of society, but the good of some mysterious entity, society as a whole, something which included but transcended the mere individuals. What was good for Germany, the Nazi Commonwealth, might be very bad for the Germans, the common people. They made the group into a person; something which science has always refused to do because it does not make sense.

The Nazis recognised, more clearly than many scientists, that science can only be concerned with the tangible welfare of real people, that the overriding personified state is not a scientific entity. They set themselves to destroy science and build up in its place a pseudo-science which would never overstep the boundaries fixed for it by their political beliefs. They persecuted scientists not only for being Jews, or democrats, socialists or communists, but for being scientists in the ordinary meaning of the term. ·

"The new science," says Dr. Bernhard Rust, Minister of Science, Education and Culture,[40] "is entirely different from the idea of knowledge that found its value in an unchecked effort to reach the truth. The true freedom of science is to be an organ of a nation's living strength and of its historic fate and to present this in obedience to the law of truth." Notice again how near the second sentence is to being true. Interpret "nation" not in the Nazi way as an entity itself, but as an organised collection of people; put, instead of "present" the words "to further and advance this in obedience to the law of truth," and one has something which science could agree to. It was the strength of the Nazis that they were sufficiently aware of the social problems of to-day to say something relevant to them; but they invariably said just the wrong thing. Always their solution, instead of carrying forward the stream of man's evolution, suggested that it should be reversed; that man should give up that hardly won control over the material world, whose highest development is science, and should become once more a barbarian at the mercy of his feelings and irrational desires.

CHAPTER VII

IS COMMUNISM SCIENCE?

Of all the political systems which are alive at the present day, communism is almost the only one whose influence is mainly due to the force of its ideas and not the mere number of its adherents. It has worked out a consistent body of theory which ties all its beliefs together with the threads of reason. That alone entitles it to careful and sympathetic examination by scientists. And their sympathy must be increased when they notice that communists profess the greatest admiration for science, and carry this admiration into effect in the Soviet Union, the only country where they have had the power to implement their ideas for more than a few months.

From being an extremely backward country in science, Russia has in twenty years become an extremely important one. In some sciences, particularly the newer ones such as genetics, it is already producing as good work as any country in the world; in older disciplines, in which other countries had already a long start over it, it has not yet been able entirely to catch up. It is often judged on an unfair standard, which neglects the backwardness of the pre-Revolutionary science from which the present development had to start. The Russian achievement should be compared with that of, say, India or South America, rather than with Britain or the United States. The illiteracy from which it has sprung, and the rapidity with which it has been forced forward, is the explanation of the undoubted scandals which have occurred, such as the success (which may now be receding) of the careerist efforts of Lysenko and Prezent, a pair of able charlatans who did much to corrupt the growth of Soviet genetics. But on any reasonable standard its achievement is remarkable; granted that some of its young men are in too much of a hurry; granted that it lacks the ballast of experienced and critical older men; but there is no possiblity of denying that it has come a long way in a short time and that more official encouragement has been given to science in the U.S.S.R. than in any other country of the world in recent years, or indeed at any time in the past.

These very practical deeds are not confined to founding research institutes and financing professional scientists. The government has used its influence to put science and reasoned thought over to the public. I quote from Haldane:[41] "The intensity of the interest taken in philosophy in the Soviet Union may be gauged by the statement, which I believe to be true, that in 1936, one hundred thousand copies of a translation of certain of Kant's works (I cannot believe they were his complete works!) were printed, and the whole lot sold out." Ruhemann, describing conditions at about the same time, writes: "Every Soviet newspaper prints leading articles on scientific and technical subjects and the results of science and engineering are front page news. . . . Well-stocked scientific technical bookshops are as frequent in Soviet towns as tobacconists are in London." This, if true, is enough to make any scientist, who is not terrified at being dragged out of his laboratory into the light of day, throw up his hat and shout.

Some of them, and some of the most brilliant, responsible and enterprising, have done so. Bernal finishes his book, *The Social Function of Science*, probably the most important book on this subject to appear in recent times, with the following paragraph:

"Already we have in the practice of science the prototype for all human common action. The task which the scientists have undertaken—the understanding and control of nature and of man himself —is merely the conscious expression of the task of human society. The methods by which this task is attempted, however imperfectly they are realised, are the methods by which humanity is most likely to secure its own future. In its endeavour science is communism. In science men have learnt consciously to subordinate themselves to a common purpose without losing the individuality of their achievements. Each one knows that his work depends on that of his predecessors and colleagues, and that it can only reach its fruition through the work of his successors. In science men collaborate not because they are forced to by superior authority or because they blindly follow some chosen leader, but because they realise that only in this willing collaboration can each man find his goal. Not orders, but advice, determines action. Each man knows that only by advice, honestly and disinterestedly given, can his work succeed, because such advice expresses as near as may be the inexorable logic of the material world, stubborn fact. Facts cannot be forced to our desires, and freedom comes by admitting this necessity and not pretending to ignore it.

"These are things that have been learnt painfully and incompletely in the pursuit of science. Only in the wider tasks of humanity will their full use be found."

This is a very fine statement of the aims and method of science, whether or not one agrees that in acting in this way scientists are behaving like communists. Other authors[42] have been even more enthusiastic, and put the relationship the other way round, claiming that communism is the application of the scientific method to political and social affairs. This is a claim which cannot be dismissed out of hand, not only because it has been made by reputable scientists, but also on account of the publicly expressed and official valuation of science in Soviet Russia. It is necessary to discuss sympathetically whether communist policy is decided by the application of scientific thought and whether that thought, supposing it to be scientific in method, is being correctly applied. I do not, however, intend to enter into detailed controversy about the tactics of the communist party as a political body in the present situation. The scientific approach, which I am trying to follow, is primarily an intellectual affair concerned with the rational basis on which those tactics are based.

SA–D

The communist system of thought, as is well known, was first worked out by Marx and Engels in about the 1860's and was subsequently developed by many authors of whom the most important are those two extremely practical men, Lenin and Stalin. The best recent English discussion of its relation to science is in Haldane's book, *The Marxist Philosophy and the Sciences*. As Haldane points out, Marxism is not a complete and finished system of dogma. "Marxism," he says, "is not complete, not a system, and only in the second place theoretical. It is not complete because it is alive and growing, and above all because it lays no claim to finality. The most that a Marxist can say for Marxism is that it is the best and truest philosophy that could have been produced under the social conditions of the mid-nineteenth century. It is not primarily a system, but a method." And he quotes Engels: "The sovereignty of thought is realised in a series of extremely unsovereignly-thinking human beings; the knowledge which has an unconditional claim to truth is realised in a series of relative errors; neither the one nor the other can be fully realised except through an endless eternity of human existence." This is a claim of exactly the same kind that science makes. It, too, knows that it has never discovered the whole truth, and that each individual can only hope by his efforts to come a little nearer than his predecessors to a full comprehension of the processes he is studying; it, too, is a method of approach, and not a final body of hard-and-fast doctrine.

In its second most important point Marxism is also in perfect agreement with science. It is a materialist philosophy. That does not mean that it believes that everything in nature is a machine in the sense that a motor-car is one, or that it is only the ultimate physical elements, atoms or electrons or whatever they may be, which are of any significance and all the rest is mere froth. It means merely that there is a world of stubborn reality which we can investigate, and which can be changed by our actions, but not by our thoughts alone. As

Lenin wrote:[43] "The sole property of matter—with the recognition of which materialism is vitally connected—is the property of being objective reality, of existing outside our cognition."

Many scientists would disagree with that statement in theory, and more would argue that it had no meaning and was simply nonsense. But, like everyone else, those who argue that the world is a product of our own minds cannot, by taking thought, add a cubit to their stature; and the people who argue that it is meaningless to ask whether a hare is real or not, would agree with Mrs. Beeton that the first step to jugging it is catching it, and that is not done by sitting down and hoping.

The next point in Marxist thought is not merely in agreement with orthodox scientific views, but is, I think, in advance of them, and states clearly and definitely an idea which science is only just beginning to recognise. Everything in the world, this part of Marxism states, is essentially and necessarily changing and developing. The typical thing one must expect to find in nature is not something like a stone, which apparently stays the same for ever, but something like a flame or an animal. As a recent non-Marxist philosopher has put it, [44] "Our knowledge of nature is an experience of activity"; but forty years before that was written, Engels[45] was already writing of "the great basic thought that the world is not to be comprehended as a complex of ready-made things, but as a complex of processes."

It is a pity that, for historical reasons, Marx and Engels chose a dialectical argument as the typical example of the process by which things interact with one another. By that is meant an argument in which one man asserts one thing, and his opponent the exact opposite. It was the characteristic method of thought of the Middle Ages, a technique which has been given a thousand-year trial and has produced practically no increase in man's understanding of Nature. But this unfortunate choice does not obscure the enormous advance which the Marxists made by their insistence that change is an essential part of the world.

Much of the recent development of science seems to have been towards a view of this kind. As I understand it, the basic ideas of modern physics, quantum mechanics and the theory of relativity, do actually describe the world in terms of processes and not in terms of static things. Certainly in biology, a field which I know more about, the process view (what is called dialectical materialism as opposed to mechanical materialism) is more or less unavoidable. Living things are not mere machines; they are essentially developing and changing things, growing from the egg to infant to adult, and dying, and linked with others in a succession of individuals which show the long-range changes of evolution. These are incontrovertible facts; but I believe biology at present under-estimates their importance, and would be well advised to give them something more like the emphasis which the Marxists urge.

The basic notions of Marxist philosophy are then almost, if not quite, identical with these underlying the scientific approach to nature; there is certainly nothing in them which could cause scientists to reject the rest of the Marxist system out of hand.

I cannot pretend to judge the value of Marxism in other fields in which I am not specially trained with the same assurance as I can in science. But one can make an attempt to apply scientific criteria to its pronouncements on economics and sociology, which are after all subjects about which everyone must have picked up a certain amount of information. In the sphere of economics even the layman can recognise that Marxist theorists foretold the coming of the crisis of 1930 at a time when orthodox economists and social scientists had no idea that it was on the way. That seems very strong evidence that the Marxist theory of economics has a great deal in it, and orthodox economists who reject it have a lot of explaining to do. Until they can show a similar success, the Marxists seem to be winning on the practical test.

It is in the Marxist theory of social action that we come to the first point where I believe that the evidence shows that they have made an important mistake; not so much a mistake of theory as one of emphasis. Marx claimed to be able to show from the study of history that the important steps in the development of human societies were brought about by the actions, not of individual men, but by large groups of people; individual kings and statesmen can only increase or decrease the speed with which the will of the dominant class in society becomes effective. There is nothing much to quarrel with in that view; the only point worth arguing about is just how effective individuals may be in speeding up or slowing down the process.

Next, Marx went on to argue that the groups which are effective in society are classes which differ from one another in their economic position, and that it is their economic status which is the most important factor in determining the direction in which they try to alter society. The class which owns the machines by which wealth can be made will want to keep them; the class which does not own them will want to get them.

It seems to me that science is bound to accept that as the ultimate explanation of the broad outlines of human history. So long as one adopts the view that human actions are caused by anything, the only things there are which can possibly act as causes for them are the material facts. If one rejects that one rejects the whole causal concept, in relation to psychology, and reduces it to a completely arbitrary subject which has no relation to the rest of nature. That is certainly not true of animals, and it would be completely unscientific to suppose that it is true of man.

But—here comes the "but"—the relation between the external world, the brute facts of existence, and what a man thinks about them, is not at all simple. Marx, living when the sciences of psychology and sociology were in their infancy, thought that one could short-circuit the complications and make the simple rule that, on the whole, men would see where their material advantage lay, and go after it. It seems to me that the facts one can observe around one show that that is not true.

The number of people who do not own the actual machines by which wealth is manufactured out of raw materials has, as Marx foretold, grown enormously. But they have not been, as he said they would be, forced down to the level of existence of the lowest wage-earning proletariat. And the greater proportion of them do not go after their immediate material interests by trying to seize control of the machines. The only place where this has happened in a big way was Russia, which, at the time it had its revolution, was at about the same, or even at an earlier, stage of economic development as the Western Europe of the 1880's, in which Marx was writing, and sociologically was still more backward. In all the other countries the development of the economic system has proceeded much on the lines Marx envisaged, but the psychological effects of this evolution of the non-owning class have been quite different from what he thought. Instead of being primarily concerned to better their economic position, which was not nearly as bad as Marx expected, the majority of them seem in practice to have been much more worried about the emotional and social chaos which capitalism produced, and which was much worse than Marx foresaw. Instead of socialist revolutions, the Fascist movement spread over practically the entire highly industrialised world except for England and America.

Such a mistake, if it is a mistake, would not deprive communism of the right to be considered a scientific movement. All the sciences have made mistakes; all that it is necessary to do is to correct the mistake and no great harm is done. But unfortunately this is a mistake which it is very difficult to put right. Communists are working as representatives of the great mass of mankind who, as they correctly deduced, would be forced out of possession of the means of making wealth. But they thought that these dispossessed would be put in the position of lowly paid wage-earners, and this conviction is so strong that they consider the wage earners as the only true working class, the only people who genuinely have lost their control over the means of production. This is not at all true. Very large sections of the middle classes are no more in control of the means of production than are factory hands; they are "the masses" just as much as are the typical proletarians.

For some reason, perhaps even because of an unconscious realisation that they have made a mistake, communists have made the service of the working class into the central focus with which their emotions and actions are integrated; and for this purpose they define the working class as the proletariat which Marx foretold. That is the fundamental reason why in my opinion, science cannot admit that communism is a scientific doctrine. Every approach to the world has its own criterion of value, some crucial test by which, in the last analysis, it judges whether to accept or reject a statement or an opinion. For science this is the critical experiment; the final test is whether a thing is true when tested in practice. For communism the final test is something else, service to the interests of the working class. It is not part of communist policy to make false statements, or to distort evidence, but they are less heinous crimes than to be a traitor to the working class; and this in spite of the fact that at least nine-tenths of even the wage earners of England do not believe in communist doctrine.

So long as loyalty to the working class is its final test of value, communism cannot claim, as it has done, to be the application of the scientific attitude to politics. That would be true even if its theory of the class structure of present-day society was sociologically adequate, and it is even more to the point if its theory is, as I suggest, incorrect. In my view, communist doctrine falls into three parts. Their scientific philosophy, which I have some competence to judge, seems to me profound, and an advance on anything which has gone before. Their economic theories I have no special qualifications to assess, but there seems to be a case for the orthodox economists to answer. Their sociological and political theories it is the duty of every citizen to judge, and in my judgment they do not fit the facts or lead to successful action in Western Europe or America.

Up to this point in the discussion, I have been using the word "communist" to mean any one who acknowledges that he consciously bases his political views on the works of Marx and Engels. This is a wider use than that sanctioned by the official communist party, which includes only those who fully accept the later political thought of Lenin and Stalin. The Stalinist communists have even less claim to be scientific politicians than have communists in general, since their views are fundamentally coloured by the particular problems that happen to have arisen in Soviet Russia. Few non-communists will forget the extraordinary contortions into which they were led by trying to follow the party line at a time when Russia (perhaps sensibly from her point of view) was trying to wash her hands of the war. In point of fact, it is rarely realised in Western Europe how different the Russian culture is from anything we are used to. The Soviet attempt to raise an illiterate and superstitious rural peasantry to the height of a great industrial co-operative nation within a few decades, and in the face of a hostile world, is a magnificent and inspiring effort. But many of the problems they have faced, and still more of the methods by which they have met them, are almost outside our comprehension. To accept every one of their political principles as applicable to Western European or American circumstances, is merely a sign of a lack of sociological imagination. And this is the more so, since it has become clear, for instance in the international debates of U.N.O., that the Russian deals with political controversy much more as an elaborate chess

From the catalogue of exhibition in the Petit Palais, 1937.

1. Leger was painting pictures like this *Landscape with Figures* as long ago as 1921. Look at the posters on the next hoarding, or the book covers in the next shop window, and you will see his influence. You are quite likely to have selected your toothpaste because the design of its packing played up the hard purity that he put across.

2. A surrealist picture by Salvador Dali. A *Paranoiac Head*, which,
placed on its side, becomes a group of negroes sitting round a hut :
two entirely separate images whose conjuction induces only a feeling
of irresponsible bemusement.

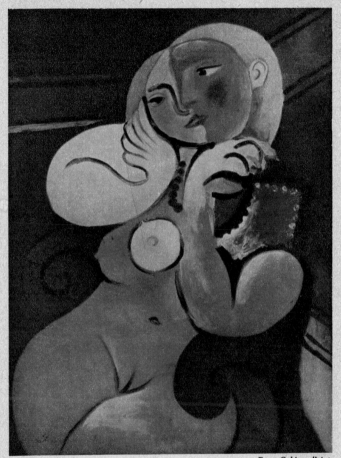

3. *Blonde* by Picasso.   He has put in the profile and full-face both at once, presumably because he liked them both, and realized that they belonged together.

From " Circle Postcards."

4. **Ben Nicholson.** A purely abstract bas-relief, which gets its effect of cheerful and undistracted elegance simply by the relations of a few plain surfaces.

5. *Breakfast*, one of Picasso's simplified, distorted sketches which yet have all the essentials ; an egg in a glass, a nice pat of butter and a roll—obviously a fine morning with no hangover.

6. *The Control Room of the Central Headquarters, London A.R.P.*, by John Piper. A picture by an abstract artist functioning as a war painter ; and he has caught exactly the rather dingy administration of technical matters which is all there was to war in the Sitzkrieg period.

7. A Surrealist picture by Paul Klee. The fantasy, as whimsical and ultimately as trivial as the Ascot hat of one of King Edward's lady friends, is exhibited with a profound originality of visual technique.

8. *Holkham, Norfolk,* by John Piper, a p
world again to find some real thing to p

n which an abstract artist has looked at the
and has found something rather romantic.

9. The Surrealist Magritte looks, matter-of-factly enough, at his meal ; and his meal looks, fixedly, at him.

By permission of the Cavendish Laboratory, Cambridge.

10. The Philips High Tension Generator for " atom-smashing "
in the Cavendish Laboratory, Cambridge. Here is the modern
æsthetic at its source. A modern sculptor like Brancusi would
have been proud of this, but his version would not have produced
2,000,000 volts.

From the Architectural Review.

11. An idealised Victorian road, with the lamp posts and the convenience as curly as the horses' manes.

12. A modern road. The "furniture," beacons, traffic-lights and so on, might have come out of a Leger painting. Besides giving us the trivial commands to stop and go, they are continually quietly reminding us that if we want to get anything done it is best not to say it with flowers, certainly not with cast-iron ones.

From " Modern Architecture," by Roth.

13. A municipal bathing place in Switzerland ; the curved roof and the mushroom pillars are a brilliant technical use of a new material, concrete ; but here the purpose of the building is simple human enjoyment.

From "*Modern Architecture*," *by Roth.*

14. Part of a Swiss housing scheme, which should convince anyone that the modern purity is not joyless or intolerant.

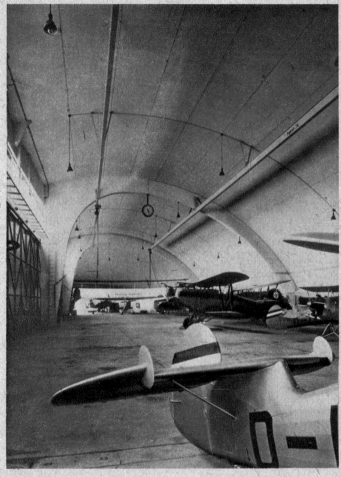

15. A Nazi aeroplane hangar. Notice the beautiful curve of the concrete shell, which is roof and wall together in one exactly calculated sweep. This is the sort of thing which persuaded the German that he had got a step beyond the old imperial eagles of Potsdam.

game—much more in the spirit one expects from Egypt or Persia, where a statement is not so much an expression of fact or opinion, but rather a pawn advanced for purposes of manœuvre—than in the somewhat more sincere way we have grown used to.

All this does not necessarily mean that science and communism must immediately part company. Although an objective view of society would seem to indicate that the Marxist conception of the working class is unsatisfactory, many of the ideals for which the communists strive in the name of the working class seem to me, as I shall argue in the next chapter, to be the same ideals as the scientific attitude would lead one to formulate. And one can accept their view that support for such proposals is more likely to be found among the non-owning than among the owning classes. The general ideological or cultural outlooks of science and of communism are, in fact, very close to one another. The reasons why it seems to me impossible to accept Haldane's suggestion that they are identical are based not on general considerations such as those which lead to the rejection of Nazism, but on some of the particular deductions the communists have made from their fundamental theory, such as their theory of the working class discussed above.

CHAPTER VIII

SCIENCE AND POLITICS

MOST people's political opinions are like those bags one meets in statistical problems; full of balls, red balls, yellow balls and true-blue balls mixed in arbitrary and unknown proportions. The scientific approach must try to treat the problem in a more orderly and systematic way. In this book I can only attempt to describe the way in which a scientific study of such matters would proceed. Its first step would be to try to decide on the aims of society; its next to define the nature of our existing difficulties, not only material but also intellectual. Only then could it begin to make a rational plan of how to unravel the knots into which we have tied our lives.

The characteristics of the scientific attitude have been discussed in different connections all through the earlier part of this book, and there is no need to go through them in detail again. The most fundamental point is that science is concerned to discover how things work, and its test of truth is that it can make them work as it wants to. In order to do this, it is necessary to adopt what at first sight seems an unduly matter-of-fact, cool attitude to many traditionally accepted ideas. Science owes no loyalty to institutions, such as, for instance, an old University or a political party. That does not mean that it must necessarily destroy such loyalties. But instead of regarding them as things valuable in themselves, and sufficient justification, without further argument, for action of some kind, a scientific attitude would regard them as feelings which fulfil certain functions in the whole psychological make-up of the persons concerned. These functions may be very important parts of a valuable attitude, in which case the traditions would be accepted by science as valuable things; but the value does not derive from them themselves, but from the fact that they are part of a mechanism which produces a valuable result.

Science derives its idea of what is a valuable result from its knowledge of the nature and behaviour of things. This sounds an extravagant claim; philosophers have been looking for a definition of value for centuries without finding one. But the scientist's idea of value is much more relative and restricted than the philosopher's. It does not pretend to be "the Good" from any absolute and final point of view. It is merely the good from the point of view of what is going on here and now. For instance, when biologists discover that animals which were once lively and active crab-like creatures have in the course of time evolved into mere shapeless sacks filled with eggs and sperm, and parasitic on other animals (*Sacculina*), they have no hesitation in speaking of this as a degeneration. By that they do not mean that the parasite is any worse than the free-living animal in the sight of God or in any absolute way; they have no views on such questions. All they can mean is that, judged by the general course of evolution as it is seen in other animals, the parasites have gone backwards and not forwards.

In exactly the same way, observation of the course of man's evolution from the animals, and of the historical development of the human personality, provides a criterion by which we can decide between advance and retreat; it gives us a direction. The most characteristic difference between the behaviour of man and that of other animals is that man can react to much more varied and much slighter differences between things, and particularly to much more subtle differences in the relations between them. A monkey can just succeed in reacting to the relation between a few boxes and a banana dangled out of his reach; he can see the point sufficiently to learn to pile the boxes on top of one another, climb on top, and eat the banana. Man, I think one would agree, can do better than that.

During the evolution of mankind from the earliest Palæolithic savages to the present day, one of the continuous developments has been man's increasing control over his surroundings, attained by the gradual application to more and more things of the orderly matter-of-fact thinking which is science. There may be other such steady progressive movements. If so, it is for someone else to say what they are. The scientist can be content to point out, what few would deny, that the increase of scientific control is one of them, and that therefore the further development of the scientific attitude is a forward movement and not a backward one.

Haldane has said:[46] "We are part of history ourselves, and we cannot avoid the consequences of being unable to think impartially." But far from trying to avoid thinking as parts of history, that is much the most important and difficult task which confronts us. It is because they deny this that one can be convinced that the Nazis were fighting against the whole weight of man's evolution.

Haldane quotes a typical example of Nazi thought, from Dr. Johann von Leers: "After a period of decadence and race obliteration, we are now coming to a period of purification and development which will decide a new epoch in the history of the world. If we look back on the thousands of years behind us we find that we have arrived again near the great and eternal order experienced by our forefathers. World history does not go forward in a straight line, but moves in curves. From the summit of the original Nordic culture of the Stone Age, we have passed through the deep valley of centuries of decadence, only to rise once more to a new height. This height will not be less than the one once abandoned, but greater, and that not only in the external goods of life."

We see once again that extraordinary and complete vacuum at the base of the Nazi edifice; for we know almost exactly nothing about the culture of the Stone Age, Nordic or not. A man who can find nothing to admire between that time and this rejects the whole of the human development of which we are conscious; and the falsity of doing so is apparent if one looks a little further, since it is just in the deepening of consciousness that man differs from the animals from which he is derived. Man is the only animal to discover the secret of getting results in this material world, which is to let one's actions be governed by an objective analysis of the situation. Our task now is to enable this analysis, which we call science, to get results when it is applied to politics.

But perhaps there is some excuse for the Nazis' muddle-headedness. There has undoubtedly been a far-reaching breakdown of the accepted standards and values on which Western European civilisation has been based. During the war we found a common purpose on a clear, though limited, objective. Now we go back to peace, and face again the conflict of ideals which so nearly reduced us to impotence before. The most definite scientific data on these comes from America. A classical account of them has been given in the two great studies of a typical American town, *Middletown* and *Middletown in Transition*. Their author[47] sums up his findings thus: "The sense of the augmented too-bigness and out-of-handness of our contemporary world is neither illusion nor merely another expression of this recurrent restlessness of man in civilisation. While unprovable because of our inability to relive intimately the moods of the past, it appears probable that we to-day are attempting to live in the most disparate and confusing cultural environment faced by any generation of Americans since the beginning of our national life." That is not true of Americans only, but of Europeans as well. Here are some of the examples he gives of conflicting social beliefs which he finds, by careful investigation, to be particularly important in the lives of Americans; it is easy to recognise them as important in one's own life, too.[48]

"1. Individualism, 'the survival of the fittest,' is the law of Nature and the secret of America's greatness; and restrictions on individual freedom are un-American and kill initiative.

"*BUT:* No man should live for himself alone; for people ought to be loyal and stand together and work for common purposes.

"2. Everyone should try to be successful.

"*BUT:* The kind of person you are is more important than how successful you are.

"3. The family is our basic institution and the sacred core of our national life.

"*BUT:* Business is our most important institution, and since national welfare depends upon it, other institutions must conform to its needs.

"4. Religion and 'the finer things of life' are our ultimate values and the things all of us are really working for.

"*BUT:* A man owes it to himself and to his family to make as much money as he can.

"5. Life would not be tolerable if we did not believe in progress and know that things are getting better. We should, therefore, welcome new things.

"*BUT:* The old, tried fundamentals are best; and it is a mistake for busybodies to try to change things too fast or to upset the fundamentals.

"6. Hard work and thrift are signs of character and the way to get ahead.

"*BUT:* No shrewd person tries to get ahead nowadays by just working hard, and nobody gets rich nowadays by pinching nickels. It is important to know the right people. If you want to make money, you have to look and act like money. Anyway, you only live once.

"7. Honesty is the best policy.

"*BUT:* Business is business, and a business man would be a fool if he didn't cover his hand.

"8. Education is a fine thing.

"*BUT:* It is the practical man who gets things done."

And so on. They are things that we all believe, sometimes;

and they contradict one another. People always have believed
contradictory things; probably no one in the history of the
world has ever had a completely consistent set of beliefs. But
there are grounds for thinking that the contradictions have
never appeared so obvious, have never been so much in the
forefront of consciousness and caused such mental strain as
they do to-day.

The evidence suggests then that the need for a coherent
and generally accepted set of beliefs is one which will have to
be met by any satisfactory solution of the political problem.
Science starts at a great advantage in meeting this need, since
many thousands of men have laboured for several centuries
to make it self-consistent.

Students of primitive cultures, investigating the social
mechanism of savage tribes and the ways in which they are
organised, have separated two main types of beliefs, both
of which have to function smoothly and without contradictions if the society is to be stable. They[49] have called them
the eidos and the ethos (Greek scholars excuse!) The eidos is
the name for the whole set of theoretical beliefs by which the
organisation of the tribe is justified. For instance, that the
God who created the tribe emerged from a certain hole in
the ground, and then mated first with a crocodile in the river
and then with a bird in the forest; and the descendants of
the first marriage belong to the crocodile totem, and those
of the second to the bird totem; and the crocodiles are fisher-
men while the birds gather fruits; or some such rigmarole.
The ethos is the system of emotional attitudes which are
socially recognised as proper in different circumstances; for
instance, that mothers-in-law are to be treated as a jest in the
music-hall, but taken seriously at home. For our society, of
course, also requires an ethos and an eidos, and much more
complex ones than are found in small out-of-the-way tribes.

Science has a perfectly good eidos to offer. In fact, it is
its duty to provide a set of reasons for all natural phenomena,
including our own behaviour. Its theoretical structure has

the advantage that it is founded on a careful investigation of the world, and will not, therefore, be easy to catch out in contradictions which might upset the smooth running of a society based on it. It has also a definite ethos, as anyone will know who has heard scientists discussing with one another. It is an ethos which allows plenty of scope for individuality. In fact it encourages people to put forward their own points of view; but it insists that they should support them by reasons which other people can verify, and that they should be willing to accept the judgment of critical experiments as to whether they have made out their case. *It is an ethos based on the recognition that one belongs to a community, but a community which requires that one should do one's damnedest to pick holes in its beliefs. I know of no other resolution of the contradiction between freedom and order which is so successful in retaining the full values of both.*

The ethos and eidos of science are things which all scientists are in substantial agreement about. There is no such agreement about the scientific solution of the economic problem, although everyone would admit that in recent years our economic machinery, particularly the machinery of distribution, has not been working as it ought. The crucial point about which controversy rages is whether this is due to the fact that in our society the incentive to production is private profit and not, at least directly, the needs of the community. Now the scientific approach definitely defines the criterion on which the merits of the two sides are to be judged. For the sociologist looking at a society, the thing which is good for the society is simply what is good for the people of the society; there is no more to it. There is no question of justifying a society by saying, as was said until a few generations ago, that it was so ordained by God, and that people should be satisfied in the station to which God has called them. Such an argument is foreign to the scientific attitude. A scientist must agree that production with a society should be production for the society as a whole. The important question for science is whether private enterprise is the most efficient method of production for the good of society as a whole.

It is probable that it has been so at some times in the past, in some places. But it was certainly not maximally efficient in Western Europe and America during the last few years before the war, and it has been unable to bring to colonial peoples, such as the Indians, the riches which the full application of modern technique could win from their countries. I think, though not by any means all scientists would agree with me, that the socialists have made out a strong case that they would be able to organise a better system. It is difficult to overlook the considerable increase in wealth in the Soviet Union, the only socialist country, throughout the twenty years during which the capitalist countries suffered an appalling depression and finished up in a war. As soon as some governmental control (i.e. socialism) was imposed on American industry in the early years of the war, its productivity leapt up at a phenomenal rate. In general the whole of evolution is concerned with the gradual increase in conscious rational control over ever more complex fields of behaviour. It seems inevitable that at some time the economic forces in society will have to be organised by human thought instead of by the automatic "laws" of supply and demand. This is in fact admitted in practice by the capitalists themselves, who have been doing their best for many years to dicker with their system by means of tariffs, quotas, price rings, etc. Their lack of success up to the present suggests that someone else should take over the job.

To talk of economic organisation, as is often done, in terms of revolution is beside the point. A revolution is a method of redistributing power, not of organising production, as one can see in the Soviet Union, which went on developing its economic machinery long after the actual revolution had been won. One can never expect to see more than one or two steps ahead in the direction of a satisfactory plan.

SA–E

No one who appreciates the problems of present-day Europe from a scientific angle can be very impressed by any solution which is primarily in political terms. The distinctions between the usual political parties—Conservative, Labour, Radical, Communist and the rest—are not, I think, of crucial importance to the scientific mind. The important line in politics is between those who judge the value of a society by its efficiency in maintaining itself and by its advance along the whole line of human evolution, and those who judge it by some other criterion, whether based on mysticism, nostalgia for the past, or motives of personal advantage.

From the point of view of science, this is the first great cleavage. All those who hold the first belief are within reach of reason and intelligent argument, while those who come into the second category can only be touched by propaganda addressed to their emotions. It is not a distinction which can be easily and automatically employed. Most people whose beliefs have an emotional basis will aver that they can produce convincing rational grounds for them; and men whose opinions are suspect because they seem founded on a trust in emotionally potent forces, such as private property, may really be expressing a rationally derived but unorthodox analysis of society. But the difficulty of using the criterion does not destroy its importance; important things are rarely easy.

The cleavage I have mentioned cuts right across the normal political parties; even, I think, across such a homogeneous body as the communists. But it is true that one is likely to find a greater proportion of non-property owners than of capitalists on the same side as science, since they will not be pushed in the other direction by motives of personal gain.

It is not likely or desirable that scientists will, as a body, set themselves the task of forming a political party. Science can only be effective as a set of ideas which permeate the public mind. The endeavour of scientists who wish to see their ideas applied in practice must be to encourage and speed up this permeation. The task is primarily one of propaganda.

Its magnitude is formidable. Only a very small number of people have a clear idea of what a scientific argument is like, and what sort of criteria a scientist uses to decide whether a thing is true enough to act on. I have in front of me a memorandum on the popular conception of the scientist. It was drawn up during the war for a group of us who were interested in the matter, and although it is not based on a comprehensive survey, it is the work of a man with considerable experience in studying the popular mind; I quote from it by his permission.[50]

"The following examples, taken at random, give a small picture of the huge barrage which, from boyhood magazines and the Wizard of Oz onwards, builds up the layman's picture of scientific method and purpose. . . . In *John Bull*, September 28th, there is an article typical of the treatment in the popular weeklies, which reach a majority of homes (about 10 per cent. of the whole population are regular readers of *John Bull*). It is headed 'THAT MAGIC SWITCH,' and starts:

" 'People still find it almost impossible to believe that they are in possession of anything they cannot see. The Power of the Mind leaves them sceptical.

" 'Any doctor will confirm that mind is master of the body. *It is now a settled principle of science.*'

"This article goes on to give a particular anecdote about a scientist. The sort of anecdote which, repeated a million times over, has produced an image of the scientist as someone removed from ordinary human realities, an almost supernatural figure:

" 'Once, when Sir Isaac Newton was giving a dinner, he left the table to get some wine. On his way from the cellar he became lost in reflection on some philosophic problem, forgot his errand and company, and was soon hard at work in his study.'

"Nearly every boys' magazine is crowded with scientific figures; the only boys' magazine which refused to deal with Martian problems has recently folded up. Usually the scientist is a brilliant, infallible, but subsidiary hero; the virile young millionaire-explorer is boss . . . Examples of the above sort of thing could be multiplied indefinitely. So could examples of the super-invention, transcending the earth, which is by no means confined to boys' magazines—e.g. the weekly with the biggest circulation of all, *Everybody's*, has as its popular strip cartoon hero Buck Rogers, the boy with the space-yacht, who defies the Moon-Priests, the Island of Doom Martians, captures girl-friend Alura from another planet, etc. . . . (speaking of a best-selling novel). Throughout the story the magnetic eyes and master-mind of the scientist operate, but, *as is nearly always the case* in such stories, the scientist never emerges with any definite character, normal activities, hobbies, political views or love life. . . . This exploitation (in advertisements) of the word 'scientific' to give prestige all helps to increase the magic of science, 'something difficult to understand but sure to be correct.' And this often actually hinders any propaganda for science by making laymen believe, but also believe that they cannot understand how the marvellously clever scientists did it. For instance, in circulating the synopsis for a recent important series of broadcast talks for adult discussion groups, on the Institutions of this Democracy, the B.B.C. gave a full explanation of all the talks except for the one talk about science, where the only comment was a note in brackets saying that this talk would be given if the subject could possibly be explained in terms which were 'not too technical.' To sum up: In general there is an enormous popular misconception about science, coupled with a considerable unorganised admiration for science as a whole and a semi-humorous, semi-reverent attitude to scientists as people."

There is not much basis there for implementing science's

contribution to political life. And the artists and writers who have been working towards what I have called the scientific attitude are in no better position to throw their weight about; the general public, I think, though I have no special data on the point, consider them just as mad as scientists and rather less useful.

But the situation is not nearly as hopeless as one might think from that report. In the first place, the social effect of a cultural movement, such as science, is very largely produced unconsciously. People who think of scientists as wizards with magnetic eyes may still, unconsciously, show an influence of scientific thought when they come to decide practical questions. Science is, after all, largely common sense; and a common-sense, matter-of-fact thinking is undoubtedly applied to a much wider range of phenomena nowadays than it used to be. Not, of course, that the range is nearly as wide as one would like. But at least the basis is there. When people discover what the method of science is, they find it is something they have known all along. They have not got the same resistance against it as they would against some totally new kind of thinking, such as Yoga.

The most effective way of convincing people of the value and usefulness of science will be the performance by scientists of a few useful and convincing pieces of analysis of social affairs. Within some fields, scientists have already shown that their particular methods of handling practical problems can become an important addition to the older techniques. You may be tempted to ask whether, when we come down to brass tacks, to actual details, the scientist's method of treating the difficulties of society would differ from anyone else's. I should answer that, in theory, it scarcely does differ from the way most practical men allege that they set about a problem; but that in practice it turns out to be totally different both in the steps taken to find out the answer, and very often in the answer arrived at. During the war, Britain made very important advances in the technique of organising the application of science to practical affairs. Probably the most systematic and important use of the new method was in the formation of Operational Research Sections attached to most of the important Commands in the Services. It is worth taking a glance at their functions and achievements, in order to see what kind of thing science can do when it comes outside the laboratory, and in what manner its results may differ from those currently accepted.

Wartime operational research had two roots. One grew up within the military machine. Some of the new devices, particularly radar, were so complicated in operation that the scientists were called from their research and development laboratories to help work out the best methods of using the apparatus in the field. It almost immediately transpired, in the very first days of the war, or just before, that the new equipment also made possible entirely new types of military operation; the whole organisation for countering a bomber raid on this country turned crucially on how quickly the raiders could be detected and the information on their course interpreted in such a way as to make it possible to intercept them. Thus the scientists, as the only people who thoroughly understood the technical possibilities, found themselves more and more forced into the consideration of matters which would previously have been thought to belong entirely to the trained military officer.

The other source of operational research was a spontaneous conviction, among a group of non-military scientists, that the conduct of military operations was bound to throw up many problems for which the scientific method of quantitative and empirical thinking would prove very valuable. This was, in fact, nothing more or less than a demand for the application of the scientific attitude as I have been discussing it in this book. It was first openly voiced in a Penguin Special *Science in War*, which came out in 1940. Fairly soon, several members of this group had got themselves accepted as scientists attached to various fighting

Commands, and, joining up with the most operationally minded radar men, they gradually built up the operational research sections.

The terms of reference of these sections were practically unlimited. At first nobody, not even themselves, knew quite what they were there for. They could do just about what they liked, provided they didn't waste anyone's time. By the time the war got properly "organised", say from 1943 onwards, there were plenty of odd corners where one could hide away a little unit of staff with comparative safety from dismissal. But these cushy spots were not, in general, on the personal staffs of the chiefs of fighting Commands; and they were by no means so common in the dark days of '40 and '41. It was during that testing time of strenuous effort that the scientists —marked men, in their civilian clothes, among the professionals of a Command staff—had to produce definite results which justified their anomalous and quizzically inspected position. They did so. As the war went on, far from being sacked, their numbers increased; the Americans copied the organisation; operational research sections were set up in other Commands than those which had first been infiltrated; and the scope and responsibility of their work within each Command increased. Science proved a useful helper in the war-making team.

There was, perhaps, no essentially new element in operational research; there were many scattered cases before the war of scientists being called on to act as practical men of affairs. The novelty in the war set-up was not in the essential nature of the work, but in its scope, in the systematic and organised turning loose of scientific method on to anything which the scientists themselves felt they could handle, and much which, at first, they were scared stiff of touching. The head of an operational research section was the official scientific adviser to the Commander in Chief, with direct access to him; and he usually attended all the Commander in Chief's staff meetings. Thus he knew exactly what problems were troubling the men responsible for taking executive action. His job was to try to help, in any way he could, in arriving at the correct decisions. Occasionally, as in the instance of radar which was mentioned above, arriving at the correct decision involved taking account of complicated technical data. But this was not always, in fact not usually, the case. Scientists turned out to be equally essential for a just consideration of quite non-technical matters, such as the relative merits of searching for submarines in the Bay of Biscay as an alternative to guarding convoys. Everyone knew that there was more chance of spotting a U-boat near a convoy (once an attack had started) than of finding one crossing the Bay. But before one can decide how to allocate one's air fleet to the various bases, one has to know *how many* U-boats are seen per hour of flying in the two regions, *how much* protection can one give a convoy in practice, *what percentage* of submarines will be sunk out of those spotted in the two areas, *how often* the weather will interfere with flying from the two bases, and a whole host of similar questions. The "science" necessary to answer most of these questions was extremely simple—merely the combing of the records, and taking averages of the past results—occasionally a very little simple algebra, or one of the conventional statistical formulæ as a little pansy trimming. Anyone, with the time, might have done it; when it was done, it had to be straight commonsense or we should never have got the Service staff to swallow it. But after all, much the same can be said of practically all science ever has done—some appears commonsense immediately it is finished, some takes a few years before it is assimilated. The actual doing of it is not much the easier for that! And the important fact for our present purposes is that, when trained scientists did not make operational analyses of this kind, usually nobody did—or if somebody tried to he either didn't know when to stop going into unnecessary detail or left some vital factor completely out of account. To do the thing continuously, responsibly, over the whole field of a Command's activities, and up to time, a team of trained research scientists was indispensable.

Military operational research still provides the best example to date of an intensive and fairly large-scale attempt to use scientific method, not merely to solve technical problems, but to help in defining and solving problems of policy. In spite of the specialised field in which it operated, the tradition and experience which operational research hammered out for itself are full of lessons for future times of peace. One of the most important of these—although it should scarcely be necessary to emphasise it—is that scientists can take part in forming policy as members of a team. Any suggestion that scientists should be allowed to use their training in fields wider than those of sheer technology, is only too often countered with the silly cry that they are demanding dictatorial powers. The expert should be on tap, but not on top, squeal some of those who are on the top now. This is primarily a reaction of fear. Scientists could only acquire undue power in the handling of public affairs in either of two conditions; if the scientific method were so overwhelmingly more efficient than other modes of thought as to put them completely in the shade, or if the non-scientists failed, from personal incapacity, to make their presence felt. Now I do believe that the scientific technique of handling events is the most effective yet invented by man, and that in consequence men trained in these methods will come to play a very large, and perhaps predominant, role in affairs. Even after only one or two years' experience during the war, Air Chief Marshal Sir Philip Joubert wrote: "One of the problems of a Commander in Chief who had an operational research section was to prevent the scientists taking over complete control of the operation of his squadrons." But the airman is really paying too fulsome a compliment to "those University types in flannel bags," as one of them called us. Not even such an advocate of the scientific attitude as I would maintain that other methods of approach have nothing to offer; and in fact the scientists never wished to take, and never came within miles of taking, control of operations. They were, knew themselves to be, and intended to remain, members of a team; with a special skill—important but not all-important—to contribute.

One of the most far-reaching characteristics of the scientific approach to a practical problem is an insistence on deciding exactly what one is trying to do. It is surprising how hard it often is to decide this. To take a fairly simple case. The Air Force convention was that the aircraft in a squadron were being properly and satisfactorily maintained if, on any day, a certain standard proportion were fit to fly. But why that particular proportion—60% or 70% or whatever the chosen figure? A number of alternative answers have to be considered. It might be that our main concern really was to ensure that there would always be enough aircraft at readiness to meet a sudden emergency. Or it might be that supplies of aircraft were short, and that particular rate of use and repair had been found the most economical in preserving them for a long life. Or again, manpower might be the crucial shortage, and the rate of maintenance be decided so as to use the available labour force as economically as possible. Until one has decided which of these alternatives is the case, one cannot start to rationalise the system. In the actual circumstances of the war, the third alternative—a tight manpower supply—was the most important factor, and the operational research sections were able to calculate new rates of maintenance adjusted to the rates of flying in different squadrons so as to produce the maximum number of hours in the air for the available number of man-hours worked on the ground. The effect was appreciable—an increase of well over 50% at the expense of no more than a little precise thought devoted to asking what one was trying to do.

In how many practical affairs of the day is this essential enquiry omitted? I will not attempt to give examples from the working of business, but I suspect that anyone who knew the facts could easily find them. But in large public questions, examples of un-thought-out objectives are legion. What, for instance, is Britain really trying to get out of the export drive? In general terms, no doubt, a higher standard of life. We export a lot of things to pay for importing a lot of other things; of the things we import, a certain number are worked on and re-exported with an added value; but there remains some residue, of wheat and bacon, pineapples, timber, steel and so on, which we actually use to raise our own standard of living. It is this residue that the whole business is in aid of. But it is extraordinarily difficult to get anyone to say just what quantities of what commodities it consists of (apart from the food items). Or consider an example on a somewhat smaller scale. What are Universities really training their students for? Are they giving a general education in culture and citizenship, or are they trying to turn out technical experts? If the former, what are the crucial lessons which can be taught in the different faculties and how are the courses related to getting these lessons across; or if the latter, what kind of experts, what proportions of the various types of specialists, and so on?

Such questions are admittedly difficult to answer. But it is usually possible to get somewhere near a satisfactory solution, and it is always worth trying. The method of approaching them must be twofold. On the one hand, there are certain very general considerations of value and ultimate objective; for instance the relative importance of imported material amenities as compared with the spiritual benefits of leisure, or of technological skill compared to a broad humanistic culture. Although such objects are not, in my opinion, entirely outside the field of scientific theory, it is in practice the non-scientists who can usually make the most important contribution regarding them. On the other hand, one must study what is actually being achieved as things are; and this is the main contribution of the scientist. Often it will turn out that our institutions are in practice producing effects which were not at all considered to be their main function. We may think of the Universities as the nurseries of culture, only to discover that they produce very few creative artists and writers, but are the seedbed from which our whole technological achievement grows. Only by combining a criticism in broad philosophical terms with a detailed assessment of the facts can one hope to reach a sensible and practical formulation of the direction which development should take.

It is from this same careful, quantitative, and laborious examination of the facts that one obtains the other two essential bases of an operational research analysis. These are two closely connected data: a survey of the resources available for use, and a description of how they are being used at present. It is only after a decision has been reached as to the end aimed at, and after reasonably complete knowledge has been accumulated about the means on hand, that the most intellectually interesting part of operational research begins. The most valuable method of analysis is usually to try to estimate the effects of introducing variations into the current practice. A complex practical operation always involves a large number of interrelated steps. The scientific method of analysis is to try to find out the relative importance of these in determining the overall rate of the whole sequence. It often demands a good deal of ingenuity to think how data can be found which will enable one to deduce the effect of varying a process at stage B, so that it can be compared with the results of a suggested improvement at stage D, say. But when quantitative methods of estimating such effects can be discovered, they make it possible to decide which are the relative bottlenecks, and where efforts at improvement should be concentrated.

All these principles, when stated perfectly generally, appear the tritest of commonsense. But in practice they would be revolutionary. Consider the problems of India, the

Colonies, or Palestine. One very large element in all those situations is the need to raise the standard of life of the local inhabitants; yet in even the most serious public discussions, this aspect of the matter is almost entirely elbowed out of sight by an overwhelming concentration on narrowly political considerations. Where can one find a clear statement even of the material objectives of Colonial development? What is it proposed eventually to do with tropical rain-forest, or the inland savannah of West Africa? How often is the future of these countries looked at against a background of a reasonably complete survey of their resources and a technological assessment of the possibilities? Yet the problem of making the tropics fit for civilised life is the largest and most exciting technological problem facing our generation—one which we certainly possess most, if not all, the knowledge necessary to solve. If it were faced with energy, and, as a first step, an adequate scientific staff were given the task of studying the material factors involved, there is no doubt that the political tensions, no longer shouting their war-cries against a background of technological silence, would appear shrunken to more manageable proportions. The lessons of the war experience are in fact just filtering through into this field. A considerable beginning was made during the operation of the Middle East Supply Centre, and the appointment of a Scientific Adviser to the Conference of East African Governors is very much a step in the right direction; but rather a small one compared with the size and interest of the issues involved.

If everything goes according to the book, one should of course expect a great increase in the application of scientific method to the economic problems of England. We have a government pledged to plan. Perhaps it is being rather querulous, but it is difficult to dispel the last traces of doubt whether the officials who have run the governmental machine for so long really know how to set about the task. The Civil Service, who must bear the brunt of examining the facts and executing the policy, were not organised for the putting into operation of major constructive efforts. Their conventional machinery is far less fitted for such an enterprise than that of the Services, which, as one finds when they get down to the bedrock job of war, are organised to concentrate on getting something done, and have special groups assigned the responsibility of deciding what to do. Moreover the currently accepted expert on planning is the economist, a man whose training is shot through and through with the assumptions of a system in which money is the ultimate criterion and goods are thought of as the mere resultants of the automatic workings of the economic machine after the controls have been set by the monetary policy. A scientific approach to planning needs a reversal of this attitude; goods are for it the essentials, and money merely a means.

These fears may be groundless; but it is not obvious that the Civil Servants who plan nationalised industries (or the entrepreneurs who ran them before) are any more above the need of scientific assistance than were the staff officers whose profession was to organise the operation of aircraft for war.

There is no reason why scientific methods should not prove helpful even in the grand political sphere of foreign affairs. Little concerted effort has yet been made to apply them to such matters, but in order to give a concrete example of one, at least, of the ways in which the scientist would try to tackle them, I shall quote at some length from an article by the Anglo-American anthropologist Bateson in the "Bulletin of the Atomic Scientists" for 1946. He is using what the operational research workers used to call "the model method"; the method, that is, of defining a mathematical system which, it is hoped, will serve as a model similar to the state of affairs under investigation, and from which the probable changes in the real situation could be deduced. Bateson sets out to discuss the progress of an armaments race between nations, to see if we can reach any deeper understanding of the phenomenon which will help us to control it. His mathematical model was actually formulated by L. F. Richardson in a paper published in 1939[31]; we will leave out the algebra, and give the discussion in Bateson's words:

"Broadly the phenomena may be summarised as regenerative (or 'vicious') circles of cause and effect, such that A's actions become stimuli for B's actions of the same type, and these in turn become stimuli for further actions by A, and so on. Stated in these very broad terms, clearly every such system might progress at greater and greater speed until it topples over into the state of war. There are, however, a number of other considerations which have to be taken into account:

"1. The relation between stimulus and action is complex and is subject to reversals of sign. In Richardson's basic equations it is assumed that A's rate of armament will be proportional to the amount of armament possessed by B. This basic equation he elaborates, examining also the implications of a system in which the effective stimulus would be, not B's total armament but that armament which B has in excess of A. The stimulus factor in the equation is then $(B-A)$, and the rate of A's armament equals $(B-A)$ multiplied by a constant which Richardson calls 'the defence coefficient'. Such an equation may satisfy these cases in which each side argues 'The other side is getting ahead of us. We must therefore hurry up.'

"This, however, is not the only type of argument which stimulates armament. There is also an argument in which the sign is reversed. 'The others are falling behind. Let's get ready to beat them up.' In this case, and also in 'The others are so far ahead of us that we had better appease them' we see a reversal of sign so that the stimulus factor which will make A arm more rapidly is now, not $(B-A)$ but $(A-B)$, and when this latter term is negative in value, we may even see 'negative aggression' in the form of appeasement.

"2. It is known that the various cultures of the world differ enormously in the degree to which they are characterised by predominance of one or other of these opposite types of relation between stimulus and aggressive activity. The 'bully-coward' motivation is one which is rather sharply disapproved in American and English life, while motivation in terms of the excess of strength held by the opponent is strongly approved in terms of 'fair play'. In Germany, on the other hand, it is expected as a matter of course that the stronger will take advantage of his extra strength and that the weaker will submit. In Russia, preliminary studies indicate that very high value is set upon achieving one's own full strength. It is not the fact that one can beat somebody else that is important but the assurance that one is exerting one's full strength. Conflict—especially conflict against an enemy who is conceived to be stronger than oneself—may help one to this assurance but conflict is by no means the only way of achieving it.

"There is thus a vast field, here, for more exact research.

"3. We must also consider the motivation which each side attributes to the other. Even though each side may be actually motivated in terms of the other's apparent extra strength and would actually slow down if they thought the others were weaker than they, each will attribute to the other the opposite type of motive. Each will say 'If we don't catch up, the others will take advantage of our weakness and will say to themselves "let's get ready to beat them up".'

"4. All the statements in 1 and 2 above require to be corrected for the fact that the stimulus term in the equations is not the real strength but the apparent strength—the strength of the others as it is perceived or imagined. This figure is subject to two main types of distortion: (a) Increase or decrease due to the actual falsification of the reports and rumours which each arming nation will give to the outside world; (b) Increase or decrease due either to persecutional fears or to unrealistic optimism, and these psychological factors certainly depend upon the cultural conditioning of the individuals concerned, and upon their realistic sureness of their own personal strength. Such a recurrent myth as that of encirclement is no recent development in Germany but is a deepseated characteristic of German thinking. For example in German fictional films we find, instead of the 'chase' so loved by Hollywood producers and American audiences, slow encirclements of the hero. The human imagination can not only exaggerate or minimise the strength of a potential enemy, it can also distort the picture of how that strength would be used.

"5. The matter is further complicated by peculiarities of the new weapons. The atomic bomb is not only a saturation weapon in the sense that when it is used the entire defence machinery of the attacked spot is dislocated. It is also saturating in the sense that a given nation need only possess a limited number—a few thousands perhaps—of this weapon to achieve 'complete' aggressive strength. The making of further thousands will not further increase its aggressive power. On the defence side, however, the picture is very different. Even adequacy of defensive preparation is probably impossible. Therefore it appears that we must expect a world in which several powers are saturated with the weapons of attack, but are still making frantic efforts to achieve some degree of efficiency in defence.

"What will be the psychological implications of this emphasis upon defence? An increasing fear of being attacked? An increasing belief that attack is the only defence? Or an increasing realisation that war has become an intolerable business? And will every people react alike to this peculiar state of affairs? To these questions, the anthropologist can hazard an answer only to the last, and to this his answer will be 'NO'. It is most unlikely that the nations will react alike. There will be profound differences between them and these differences will be related inter alia to each people's special habit of response to contexts involving strength and weakness, attack and defence. Just how these differences will be expressed we cannot say without further research, but we can warn that the nations will certainly misinterpret each other's behaviour and that it is unlikely that these misunderstandings will be of such a kind as to promote goodwill between them.

"6. In addition to the factors which make for increased rate of armament among the nations, there is, as Richardson points out, one important factor which tends to diminish this rate, namely the expenditure which each nation must make to keep up the pace. His equations therefore contain a negative term in which the total strength of the arming nation is multiplied by a 'fatigue and expense coefficient'. Supposing these equations to be substantially correct at least for moderate disturbances—Richardson has analysed a series of armaments races and demonstrated surprising regularity—we may then follow him in assuming that whether the system will move toward a steady state or toward infinite armament, will depend upon a rather simple relation between the constants involved. If we adopt the simpler form of the equations and consider the case of two nations, equilibrium will occur if the product of their 'fatigue coefficients' is greater than the product of their 'defence coefficients.'

"In terms of this analysis, the result of the atomic discoveries and other great advances in the machinery of destruction can be stated very simply. It has been to reduce the 'fatigue coefficients'. A nation can now become infinitely prepared to destroy its neighbours (though not prepared to defend itself) for the modest sum of less than five billion dollars. The likelihood that the system will reach equilibrium in Richardson's sense is therefore very much reduced, though it is conceivable that the nations, having achieved infinite aggressive armament, might stand glaring at each other for an indefinite period without actual war. But the fact that the techniques of rapid attack have so far outstripped those of defence make us doubt whether such a balanced position could be stable. In such a case, it would be too easy for any nation to succumb to the argument, 'If we attack, the enemy will immediately become weak. Let us therefore beat them up', and too easy also, for each side to fear that the other may be on the point of arguing in this way."

This discussion of various types of operational research

will perhaps give some hint of the way in which scientific method could be applied to the major problems of society. There are many difficulties to be overcome before such work is undertaken, and its results put into practice, on a scale commensurate with our needs. Not least is the difficulty of persuading sufficient mature and first-class scientists to leave their laboratories and launch out into this uncharted sea. But not until the attempt is made, on a large scale, can we say that we are dealing with the social life of man (which is most of his life) in a fully responsible way.

CHAPTER IX

LIVING IN A SCIENTIFIC WORLD

WHAT would the world be like to live in if the scientific attitude did become generally accepted as the directing force of our culture? Most people, we are told, think of it in terms of Buck Rogers and his space yacht, and even the more sophisticated will have their imaginations full of Kipling's *Aerial Board of Control*, or Huxley's *Brave New World*, or some of Wells' more aseptic novels. They are likely to think that even if science could give the Open Sesame to all the riches of Ali Baba's cave, it wouldn't be worth much if the only furnishings were dentists' chairs, complete with drills. It seems as if there would be no place, in the chemically purified scientific world, for the ordinary little enjoyments of life, playing bridge or darts, messing about with a bonfire in the garden.

These fears are two hundred years out of date. In science's early days it could only handle the most simple things; it had to reduce an action like standing a fellow a drink to a matter of giving him a certain quantity of diluted ethyl alcohol of a certain strength. But those days are long past. Science realises now that every detail of human life is extremely complicated; it is connected with every other detail by innumerable threads of habit and custom, of economic interest and emotional feeling. A way of life is a network, full of cross connections. It is worth giving an example of how sociologists try to analyse social behaviour; it will show, I think, that they do not disregard all the colour which gives sparkle and interest to life. In fact, they see so many things involved in even the simplest actions that it is at first difficult to follow what they are driving at. One has to try to look at one's own behaviour from outside, as they have been able to look at the behaviour of men in savage tribes.

Consider, then, going out with your wife in the evening to friends, perhaps to play bridge. According to Bateson, the factors involved are (I will give the technical names):

1. *Structural.*—Concerned with how the society is built up; for instance, that wives are equals with their husbands, and accompany them to social functions on equal terms, instead of staying at home, or coming to act as servants.

2. *Eidological.*—Concerned with the way people think in that society; for instance, they think of their acquaintances as human beings like themselves, with faults and virtues, desires and feelings and so on, but not as potential witches to be on one's guard against, or as mere ciphers in an elaborate ritual of politeness.

3. *Affective.*—Concerned with the emotions and feelings involved in the meeting, the friendship for the people visited, the gaiety or sobriety of the party.

4. *Ethological.*—Concerned with the general system of feelings which society considers appropriate; that one behaves politely to people one doesn't know too well, but may take more liberties with intimate friends; that a certain amount of assertiveness and drive is expected from men, but that women should be more homely and sympathetic.

5. *Sociological.*—Concerned with the stability and integration of society; friendly visits bind people together with bonds of common interests and affections.

6. *Economic.*—Perhaps you are taking your wife to call on the boss, and the impression you make will affect your chances of promotion.

7. *Developmental Psychological.*—Concerned with the education which has brought you up to be a person who likes to go out for casual enjoyment, instead of someone tormented by conscience, which might drive you to spend the evening in prayer, or someone with a passion for improving

your mind, so that you would rather stay at home with a
course from a correspondence college.

No one would pretend that those were all the factors involved in your bridge party, but they are enough to start
with. Science does not consider the whole thing simply as
changing the space-time co-ordinates of a few bits of paste-
board. It acknowledges that it is a part of life, and must be
handled with the gentleness which that makes necessary. It
is the present ferocious monkey-house civilisation, brilliantly
scientific in spots and plain brute in others, which really
threatens the quiet and comfortable life, even in times of
so-called peace. As an American poet has written.[52]

> They are able, with science, to measure the millionth of a millionth
> of an electron volt.
> THE TWENTIETH CENTURY COMES BUT ONCE.

> the natives can take to caves in the hills, said the British M.P., when
> we bomb their huts.
> THE TWENTIETH CENTURY COMES BUT ONCE.

> .   .   .   .   .

> the lynching was televised, we saw the whole thing from beginning
> to end, we heard the screams and the crackle of flames in a sound-
> proof room.
> THE TWENTIETH CENTURY COMES BUT ONCE.

> You are born but once;
>   you have your chance to live but once;
>   you go mad and put a bullet through your head but once.
>   THE TWENTIETH CENTURY COMES BUT ONCE.

>   Once too soon and a little too fast;
>   once too late and a little too slow, just once too often.[59]

That's not what we want to go back to now the war is over.
But however much one may point out that a world imbued
with a scientific outlook would be tolerant, sympathetic and
sincere, there will remain many people who will regard the

whole thing with horror. The old ways in which one was brought up have an extraordinary hold, and for many people any idea of change is hateful. It is resented with an intensity altogether out of proportion to the actual effect, as far as the outsider can judge, which it is likely to produce on ordinary lives.

A society, in fact, does not behave entirely like a rational human being. As Ruth Benedict[53] says, "Tradition is as neurotic as any patient; its overgrown fear of deviation from its fortuitous standards conforms to all the usual definitions of the psychopathic." So it is probably stupid to expect any new way of life, whatever its advantages over the old, to be thankfully accepted even by all the people to whom it will most obviously do good. Trying to cure the ills of society is rather like dosing a cow; you want one man to hold its mouth open while another blows the pill to the back of its throat down a cardboard tube; and it has the same danger, that the cow may blow first.

Advocates of a new order have to expect more or less violent opposition. They may console themselves, if they have confidence in their remedy, by a fact revealed by the psycho-analysts, and, I think, confirmed by common sense. People only object really strongly and irrationally to something if it touches a part of their personality which is out of order, which they would themselves object to if they could dare, or could make the effort, to face it. Their "instinctive" rage at the new proposition is so intense only because they really know there is something in it, but do not want to let themselves see it.

Of course, the same thing applies the other way round—to the advocates of the new conception. They become preachers; people who make too much fuss and shout too loud. The louder they shout, the more coldly the others turn them down; and the more indifferent and cloddish, or the more rancorous and spiteful, the rest of the world seems, the shriller they yell. An unlovely but ordinary process, for which sociologists have coined the unlovely but out-of-the-way phrase, complementary schismogenesis[54]; something difficult to cope with, both in pronunciation and actuality.

The character of the scientific world, as a place for the ordinary man to live in, will depend enormously on how far this process of mutual blackguarding has gone before the new ideas become firmly accepted. If it is comparatively mild, the world will be a fairly easy-going and tolerant place; if it becomes virulent, the scientific attitude will be forced into a crusading, revolutionary ardour which is foreign to it, and which will make it a much less equable climate of opinion for those who do not share its enthusiasm.

There is no reason, *of an intellectual and cultural kind*, why this should happen in England or America. In both places the scientific spirit is already a powerful influence, and there is no other alternative outlook on the world which seems strong enough to cause much friction; science's battle with the only other strongly entrenched system of thought, that is to say, religion, is now ancient history.

But, of course, the snag is that other things are not equal. A scientific reorientation of society would involve economic changes, and anything of that kind is sure to be resisted by most of the people who are adversely affected by it. At the present time it is the economically strongest forces which must be challenged and tamed; their strength is such that their resistance is certain to be, in fact already is, powerful and tenacious. In England the battle has most probably been won. Under the stress of war all industries had to be controlled and their operation centrally planned in outline. Although they remained in "private ownership", the actual meaning of that phrase became altered so that many rights which owners had previously enjoyed were taken over by the state. Soon after the war a Labour Government came to power before the owners had got back all their old freedom of action; and it now seems very unlikely that they will ever do so. The dense industrial system built up on this island, much too small to feed the working hands required, was always an unstable arrangement, and its former prosperity depended largely on a huge accumulation of overseas investments; now that we have spent these in fighting two wars, the adjustment of our industrial machine is going to remain for many years too tricky a matter to be trusted to the hit-or-miss operation of the law of supply and demand and the vagaries of private profit.

The same is true of the whole of Europe, including France. But the process has not gone so far in the United States, and no one can say whether the essential control over production will pass into the hands of the consumers peaceably, or whether it will come to a fight. At present the capitalist interests seem to have been successful in persuading most Americans that socialism is the work of the devil, instead of merely meaning control by the people. In any case, Americans occupy such a huge chunk of the fertile temperate zone, in comparison with their numbers, that they are far removed from the practical need to make the best use of their resources which faces Britain and France. Their drive towards socialism will come (apart from war) from a breakdown in the profit machinery, such as produced the pre-war Depression.

It is impossible here to discuss all the detailed plans which have been put forward for the rationalisation of society, and in any case the details will have to be worked out in practice by trial and error. But there are some general results which seem to follow from the scientific view which are worth mentioning.

Perhaps the most important is that scientific investigation makes it quite clear that, just as we were finding it impossible to get into use much of the wealth which we created, so we were also wasting our human resources to almost the same degree. For instance, in a pre-war study of the English educational system, [55] it was found that, among the able pupils, 10 per cent came from upper class families (large business men and professional men), about 40 per cent from the middle class (shopkeepers, clerical workers and skilled workmen) and 50 per cent from the lower classes (manual workers). All these could have been greatly profited by a higher education; but although in the upper class practically every able child, and an equal number of not-so-clever ones as well, obtained such an education, in the lower class less than a quarter of the bright ones went through a secondary school, and in the middle class the situation was only slightly better. Over half the children who would have profited from a good education failed to get one. This wastage of intellectual ability is an inefficiency comparable to the shockingly low standards of nutrition which we have put up with. No technically competent biologist would tolerate it in his rat colony for a week, and a pig business which treated the swine like that would be bankrupt in a couple of seasons, unless it was subsidised by some Pig Board or other.

It is clear that a scientific society, which had at heart the good of the community as a whole, would enormously increase the opportunities for education. Post-war Britain is, indeed, making huge efforts to build more schools and to send more children to them and to the Universities. It is, on a long term view, perhaps the most important of all our enterprises at the present time. Further, a scientific society will have to be organised so that the able, having received an adequate training, could come to the top and use their abilities in the positions of power and responsibility. This would mean an enormous change in the distribution of power; the children of our upper classes, the professions and big business men, contribute only one-tenth of the community's supply of able men, but a much higher proportion of its influential people. If power were to be in the hands of those best able to use it sensibly, nine-tenths of it would go to the offspring of the middle and lower classes. In a scientific society, "power would be in the hands of the people."

In practical terms the problem is more complicated than

is suggested by that slogan. Although it is the great bulk of
the population, the lower and middle classes, which give rise
to the greater part of our potentially able children, they suffer
at present from the lack of proper education. It is not clear
that it would be a good plan to put too much power directly
into the hands of partially trained people, however clever.
On the other hand, if it is left where it was, largely in the
control of a richer and more privileged class, there is no
reason why the wastage of ability should not continue more
or less indefinitely.

One of the possible ways of getting over this difficulty has
been followed in Russia. During the Revolution, in which
power was taken over by the workers, the way in which the
power was used was actually decided by a highly trained
group of men. The policy of the workers was vague; the
communists, acting on the workers' behalf, put it into definite
and practical shape. It was lucky that such a group was
available, and contained some men of genius—Lenin,
Trotsky, Stalin and others. They at least did not believe in
witches or the efficacy of crossing oneself as a way of dealing
with difficult situations. They could, and did, build a society
which provided opportunity for the able but poor man to
become educated. They should soon be able to trust the
common sense of the population sufficiently to throw the
doors to power open to everyone, in a truly democratic way.
In fact, they say they are already doing so, but news about
Russia is so obviously prejudiced in one way or the other
that it is impossible for the ordinary person to be certain
what is happening.

The actual mechanism by which power will be distributed
will depend too much on particular political circumstances
for science to have any fixed ideas about it beforehand. But
it is a necessary characteristic of a scientifically organised
society that its class structure should be much looser than at
present. This does not mean that classes will disappear
entirely and everyone be on an exactly equal footing; but

social esteem will be given to a man for different reasons than it is to-day; not because he has a stake in the country in the sense that he can put a good deal of its wealth into his own pocket, but because he seems likely to contribute more than most people to the aims which society has in view. And in any case the differences in social status between people will be much less permanent and unalterable when it is possible for everyone to develop his potentialities to the full.

"Race" is another of the ways of dividing up mankind which, very important in our civilisation at present, would be very much less so in a scientific world. Not that science believes that all men are racially alike. What we know about human heredity shows conclusively that they are not. But, firstly, the scientific races do not correspond with political groups; Frenchmen from Alsace are racially much more like Germans from Baden than like other Frenchmen from Normandy. None of the great nations consists of a pure race or anything approaching it, and there is therefore no justification for making a new nation for every little so-called "racial" group, like the Slovenes or Ruthenians.

"What really binds people together," says a scientific student of man, Ruth Benedict,[56] "is their culture—the ideas and standards they have in common." Where a group of people have a common culture which is somewhat different from that of their neighbours, they should, other things being equal, be able to live their own lives in the way they please; but that is no reason for allowing them to set up tariff walls around themselves, or to go to the absurd lengths of war. Modern means of communication and transport, bringing power from where it is cheap to places where raw materials are available, have enormously increased man's productive capacity. It is ludicrous that this should be stultified, and people go hungrier than they need, because different groups have different fashions in haircutting; but that was the condition of the world before the war. It would, perhaps, cause still more ribaldry among the brutal and licentious

Gods of Olympus if the United States and the Soviet Union, blow each other (and us) to bits with atomic bombs, not because either wants to, but because each is afraid the other is just going to; but that has a fair chance of being the condition of the world in this alleged peace.

With the defeat of the Nazis and their scientifically childish theories, nationalism rather than racism has become the most dangerous intellectual and moral drug which tempts the modern man to discard his precarious hold on sanity. Those capitalists who are fond of pointing at red bogeys— and those communists who expose the aggressive machinations of the imperialists—should reflect that neither of their opponents would constitute any general danger provided they would only agree to stay at home. Economic theory cannot be a threat to regions of the world which do not accept it until its adherents try to spread it; and it can only carry the physical threat of war—which is what the world fears now—when it becomes allied with the central national governments which control the war-making machines. Those who wish to continue in their devotion to nationalism will, however, try to diminish the force of this by arguing that it is in the nature of capitalism (or communism as the case may be) to take control of national power and use it as a weapon for ends which arise, not from nationalism, but from the economic theories, which are paramount. Nationalism, they urge, is an estimable sentiment—no danger to anyone—when it is not debased and brutalised by false social and economic theories.

This apology for nationalism is, in my judgment, neither wholly true nor wholly false. Nationalism is too complex a sentiment, and is involved with too many aspects of our emotional and political life, to be dismissed so simply. A scientific evaluation of it must start with a more serious attempt to understand its nature—and when a scientist speaks of "understanding the nature" of something, he is thinking of a study of the causes which bring that thing about, and the effects which it produces. This book is no place to attempt a full scientific investigation of the modern concept of nationalism, but one can see almost at first glance that at least three different elements are usually lumped together under that name, each fundamentally important. There is, first of all, the sense of a national way of life—the feeling of being an Englishman, an American or a Frenchman, the sense of community for which one feels homesickness. That is something quite different from the conception of the nation as a unit of power, either as the sovereign ruling force in internal affairs, or as a piece on the chess-board of power politics. This power element is the second major factor in the concept of nationalism. The third which I should distinguish is one which is, perhaps, less generally recognised as distinct from the other two. It is the concept of the nation as an object of fierce patriotic devotion. It is the growth in recent times of the belief that the nation can properly demand the complete, or almost complete, submission of its individual members to the national purpose which has made Nationalism into a world menace.

This element in the mixture is of tremendous importance even when it does not go so far as an outright admission that the individual exists for the nation, and not the nation for the individual. It was the root of the jingo Imperialism of Britain forty years ago, in the time of songs like "Land of Hope and Glory"; it is the root now of the paradoxical synthesis of isolationism and imperialism which has been achieved, in ways which are superficially different but fundamentally very alike, in America and Russia; it is the root also of much of the intransigence of political movements of liberation from Albania to Indo-China. It is, in fact, the most obviously important aspect of nationalism. We must be on our guard against thinking we have accounted for it, or even excused it, when we have in fact only discussed the other two factors; and this is a common mistake of discussions which treat of nationalism in general without analysing that concept into its constituent elements. It is essential to consider the specific role of this factor which we may call "authoritarian nationalism", and to find out how, if at all, it is related to the other concepts which we commonly associate with it under the same name.

The study of "national character", the first of our three elements, has recently been tackled with some success by anthropologists. They have investigated its nature in the truly scientific way—by analysing the causes which bring it about. The classical study in this field is that of Mead and Bateson on the Balinese[57]—a group of people chosen, not because of their intrinsic importance in the modern world, but because their national character, with which they feel at home, is one which seems exceedingly foreign, and therefore easy to grasp, to the English or American eye. The fundamental principle of Mead and Bateson's approach was to observe (with all the paraphernalia of cinema shots, dictaphone recordings and so on) the processes of social interaction by which the young Balinese child is moulded, by the adults and other children with whom it is in contact, into an example of the general pattern.

There is no room here to give anything like a complete picture of the Balinese, but it is worth while to pick out one or two points to serve as examples of the method. One of the first things that struck Mead and Bateson about the Balinese was their dependence on a very complex framework into which everything has to be fitted. They are continually referring to the points of the compass; the language in which they speak to one another varies according to the castes of the two speakers; and they use, simultaneously, weeks of one, two, three and so on up to ten days. "In a strange village, where he does not know the cardinal points or the local customs, and if he does not know what day it is in at least three of the inter-cogging weeks, nor the caste and order of birth term (i.e. first, second or third child) for the person with whom he is trying to converse, the Balinese is completely disoriented. . . . If one takes a Balinese quickly, in a motor car, away from his native village so that he loses his bearings, the result may be several hours of illness and a tendency to deep sleep." This profound reliance on convention has many roots in the way Balinese children are brought up. One simple, but probably significant, fact is that a Balinese child is taught to walk by being given a framework which it walks round and uses as a support—if it wanders away it falls down. In contrast to this, we usually put our children in a square play-pen, which encourages them to keep to the outermost edges of their play-area instead of to the centre of it. The Balinese mother, in fact, gets very alarmed if her child strays out into an open space, and usually shouts some scare-word ("snake", "wolf", "dragon", or anything else which comes into her head) until the baby comes back in alarm. This method of controlling the child by frightening it is very characteristic of Balinese upbringing, though perhaps "fright" is not quite the right word; "startle" gives a rather better idea. The emotion is very common in grown-up Balinese: they have quick, timorous reactions, rather like deer. And they obviously find this emotion not altogether disagreeable; after all, it was originally something they learnt by sharing it with their mother when they were in her arms.

It is easy to understand why the Balinese, so easily startled if they lose touch with their well-known background, find their greatest pleasure in gay and lively crowds. They like things to be, as they call it, "rame", a word which can be translated as "noisily, crowdedly festive". "Pressed tightly against the steaming bodies of strangers, the air heavy with scent and garlic and spices, and many rare forms of dirt, sharing no single emotion with those so close to him, the Balinese watches the play and revels in the occasion, when he can stand completely remote in spirit, yet so close in body to a crowd."

In that description of Balinese fun, the authors bring out

another of the silent features of their national character—
the lack of human warmth and personal contact. It is probably the most interesting thing about them, because it is in
connection with the characteristic attitude to personal
relations—whether they are seen on a basis of co-operative-
ness or of dominance and aggression, of rivalry or of
emotional response—that the problem of national character
is most pressing in the world to-day. And Bateson and
Mead's analysis of this aspect of the Balinese character is
particularly full and enlightening. They show how it is
developed by a self-perpetuating system in which the adults
have been brought up to be people who are bound, by their
own characters, to bring children up just like themselves.

Balinese adults have been trained not to like warm,
personal, human contact; they have learnt to withdraw, to
sink back into themselves, if anything of the kind threatens.
So they treat their children in just that way. Mothers play a
great deal with their babies; in fact, according to our ideas
they over-stimulate them and poke and tease them for the
fun of making them smile and "coo". But as soon as the
baby, or young child, begins to show any signs of real
emotion, either of affection or rage, the Balinese mother turns
to something else and leaves the baby's response hanging in
the air. In the gay chattering family life, the child's emotions
are continually being stimulated and then frustrated—until
after a time the quite young toddler learns to keep them to
himself.

There is a fairly definite sequence of stages in a Balinese
baby's life. First he is the new-born of the family, his mother's
most darling plaything; in fact everybody is ready to tease
him all the time. His mother will flirt with him in an openly
sexual way, ruffling up his penis and saying how handsome
he is; or, to tease him, she will borrow someone else's baby
and pretend to have transferred her attentions to it. But it is
all play; if the child reacts either by affection or rage, the
mother turns away and starts laughing about something else.

Then a new baby is born; and the previous favourite becomes still more a mere butt for teasing. By the time still another baby appears, is it any wonder that the little child has become a self-sufficient creature who never gives himself away? If the child is a girl, at this stage she begins to be used as a nurse to look after the newest baby; a boy soon takes charge of an ox, and spends his time herding in the fields where he has little contact with the rest of his family.

The process of damping down the child's spontaneous emotional reaction, of teaching it, above all, to avoid carrying anything to a climax, does not go entirely smoothly, as might be expected. Children who are just getting to the stage of complete control usually pass through a phase of extraordinary tantrums or of sulks. In a final attempt to get some reaction out of their mother, they go off into tempests of rage, yelling and throwing themselves about—or they sit and ostentatiously sulk. Neither tactic is often successful; the tantrum evokes no answering rage, and the sulking child is merely neglected. After a few years of this, the child has been formed into an individual who will treat the next generation of children just as it was treated itself—the system is self-supporting.

An analysis in similar terms could be made of other national characters; in fact the task was begun by American anthropologists during the war in order to guide the government services concerned with propaganda and morale (see for instance the article on Japanese character in Penguin *Science News I*). But these studies only help us to understand what one might call the "community temperament" or "climate of personality" characteristic of a human culture. They do not go far in accounting for the exclusive and aggressive features of nationalism at the present time. It is only in a few out of the way cultures (such as some savage tribes) that the national character favours individuals who behave in the unprincipled and competitive manner exhibited by nations on the world stage. The seeds of the most

dangerous aspects of nationalism must be looked for else-
where than in those social processes which produce the
simple feeling of being at home among one's neighbours.

The fact that nations are units of power, which we mentioned as the second major aspect of nationalism, has its
roots, of course, in a long process of political development
which has been often and copiously analysed in historical
writings. As was stated earlier (Chapter VII), it seems
plausible to suppose that fundamentally, social power is
derived from the production of goods and services of social
value, and that the broad outline of political history, complicated though it is by the tortuous ways in which the human
mind can cover up and distort the ultimate realities, should
in the last analysis be expressed in terms of economic
relationships. But nationalism, as we have seen, is by no
means a matter of power politics alone; and although an
economic analysis may reveal the sources of the political
power which is now attached to nations, and even explain
why it is to the national unit, and not to some other, that
the power has been attached, it does not account for the
actual geographical entities which nowadays constitute the
nations. Before and between the last two wars, for instance,
the fundamental economic structure of Western civilisation
was based on groups, such as the capitalists, the industrial
managers, the workers and so on, which spread through
many different nations. But this internationality of economic
structure had almost no effect on the power struggles of the
nations. Even Britain, so often looked on as the centre of
international imperialism, was quite unable to prevent other
nations starting a war, although Britain's entire economic
structure was founded on the essentially peace-like activity
of world trade. Political power was in the hands of nations;
and national boundaries did not coincide with boundaries
of economic interest. Neither did they coincide simply with
linguistic boundaries; Great Britain was one nation when
it still included large numbers of Welsh and Gaelic speaking

people. Nor are national frontiers to be explained simply in terms of "national character"; there is at least as much difference between a New Englander, a man from Chicago and a Texan as between a Flemish Belgian, a Dutchman and a German from Hamburg.

The demarcation of the earth's surface into regions, which are now called nations, seems in fact to have been brought about largely by a series of historical accidents. A government, by some means or other, acquires power, happens to regulate the relations between people living in a certain area; that makes it the ruler of the internal affairs of its country. But this internal power does not necessarily mean that the national government is the seat of all power in external affairs affecting several nations. Through much of European history, for instance, the external power of national governments was no greater than, if as great as, that of the Church; and to-day in federations such as the United States or the Soviet Union, a great deal of internal power is in the hands of states which possess practically no external power at all. The pre-eminent position which the nation now occupies as the overwhelmingly most important seat of power in world affairs must be explained in some other way. And in fact the explanation must be sought in the third element in nationalism, which we called the authoritarian.

The origin of this third element is the imperfection of the human mechanism of social evolution. Man's society is founded on the training of the young in certain moral principles which embody the rules required to regulate the interaction between people in such a way that social life can continue. The forces of egoism which these principles have to restrain are very deep-seated; but in the human family and the relations between parents and children, man has evolved a mechanism which makes it possible to convey the essential moral principles at a very early age, when there is still a chance that they can gain control. The drawback of the mechanism is that it occurs mainly in the most early developed and primitive parts of the mind, which in adult life are usually hidden in the unconscious. Thus the strains and stresses which inevitably arise during the taming of the human animal into a well-behaved member of society often express themselves in highly devious ways. The most important of these maladjustments, from our present point of view, is a tendency to a morbid worship of some source of power which is substituted for that of our parents who originally imposed the social decencies on us. There is an almost universal craving to find some outside body or thing to which a man can attach his feelings of loyalty and submission. It may be a Church, or a less mundane God, it may be a political party, it may be an ideal (I shall argue in the last chapter that it might be science itself); but at the present day it is frequently a nation. The reasons for the fashionableness of the nation as a peg on which to hang these unconscious emotional needs require much more careful investigation than they have yet received. But the immediately important fact is that, among all the possible things which emotionally appear as sources of power, it is the nation which the spirit of our age chooses to pin its hopes and loyalties to.

It is this choice of the nation as the main emotional authority which poses the most difficult task for statesmanship to-day. Everyone admits the urgent necessity to set up an international authority with power to prevent the nations going to war. If this were a mere matter of constitution-making, there should be no great difficulty in devising a system which would guarantee the rights of all the peoples. We have the examples of Switzerland, the United States and the Soviet Union in each of which men of the most diverse national characters live together under an authority which preserves a reasonable degree of order and at least prevents them going to war with one another. But any effective international authority of this kind must inevitably reduce the power of the present nations; and so long as men's unconscious emotions find satisfaction in the idea of national power, they will resist the growth of international government.

We still know far too little of the psychological and social mechanism involved to be able to offer a reliable prescription of how best to proceed. It seems fairly certain that nothing will be accomplished merely by stating (as Emery Reves has done so urgently in his book *The Anatomy of Peace*) that nations must give up some of their exclusive sovereignty. Possibly the historians, who have studied the transition from rule by the feudal nobility to rule by a single king, may be able to suggest how a new loyalty to a larger organisation can be brought into being. One suspects that the process will involve one of those self-reinforcing mechanisms so common in biological and social affairs; that men will not transfer their allegiance to a new authority unless that is already supported by considerable power, while the authority cannot obtain effective power until enough men have given it their loyalty. A situation of that kind is not such a complete impasse as it suggests at first sight. But to move it, it is necessary not to rely on any single angle of approach, but to attack it from all sides simultaneously; organising and strengthening those sources of social power which stand behind it (in the present instance all the common people who hate war and the international economic and "non-political" organisations) while at the same time helping forward the battles of the fledgling ruler (the United Nations) against its older competing sovereignties, and doing everything possible to weaken the hold which these out of date symbols (the nations) have over men's emotions.

Another major change in man's emotional orientation which seems to be demanded by the recent evolution of civilised society is the reduction in his taste for big-city life. There are many reasons why huge metropolitan agglomerations like London and New York seem to be unstable arrangements, doomed in the nearish future to break up and become scattered more widely over the land. They have been best discussed by Lewis Mumford, in his book, *The Culture of Cities*. Here are some of them. When a city becomes too big, its land values rise so high that rents can only be earned if people are herded together in incredible congestion. Traffic in the rush hours is snarled up and jammed to such an extent that in New York, for instance, it is estimated that about £100,000 a day is lost on this account alone. The slums breed disease; health services in American cities of over a million cost three times as much per head as in smaller cities, but even then do not bring the mortality rates down so low as in them. The same is true of crime; large cities spend more on their police, and still have more criminals. And the city, which should provide the opportunity for wider and more varied human contacts, becomes, when it is a huge metropolis, a cold and unfriendly place, in which people can be more lonely than in a village.

Biologically, big cities are not self-supporting. Their birth-rate is too low. Metropolitan life does not encourage big families, and this applies to new industrial areas as well as to older cities. It is only the constant flow of people from the country into the towns which enables the big cities to remain constant in numbers, let alone to grow in the phenomenal way they have recently. But now the process is bringing about its own end. The fashion for small families has spread from the town to the country, and the supply of possible new immigrants to the cities is tapering off. "One is driven to ask," write two students of the problem,[58] "whether it is possible to maintain a stationary population in a community where urban congestion is sufficiently prevalent to dictate the *mores* of family life." The cities are sucking the whole life out of the country and sterilising it. "This metropolitan world," says Mumford,[59] "is a world where flesh and blood is less real than paper and ink and celluloid. It is a world where the great masses of people, unable to have direct contact with the more satisfying means of living, take life vicariously, as readers, spectators, passive observers; a world where people watch shadow-heroes and heroines in order to forget their own coldness or clumsiness in love, where they behold brutal men crushing out life in a strike riot, a wrestling ring or a military assault, while they lack the nerve even to resist the petty tyranny of their immediate boss." That is pre-war stuff; how much better the people really are than this has been made magnificently obvious when they were given a chance to show their mettle in the defence of their homes against bombing. It is only the mad hustle of an overgrown city which, in the "normal" times of peace, finds no use for the courage and endurance of air-raid wardens and fire fighters or the cheerful friendliness of the crowded shelters and tubes.

The reaction against city life has already started. It, too, can go in two ways, the Nazi or Fascist way, and the scientific. The Nazis wanted to take the unemployed out of the cities and turn them into peasants, to win a meagre living from the soil without the aid of farm machinery or supplies of power. The alternative way depends on the decentralisation of industry, making full use of modern means of distributing power wherever it is required, and of the best techniques of communication to keep widely separated factories or offices in touch with each other. The best example of it to date, perhaps, is the planned development of the valley of the Tennessee river in America under the Tennessee Valley Authority set up by the Government.

The huge tract of country drained by the Tennessee was in a bad way, constantly subjected to devastating floods, with its soil, unintelligently cultivated by poor and backward farmers, being washed and blown away by storms. The Authority, T.V.A., tamed the floods by building dams, used the water-power to generate electricity, distributed this power in a grid to towns and villages, encouraging new industries to be set up in the local townships, and making it possible for the farmers to buy farm machinery and to cultivate their land more successfully and less wastefully. They explain their functions thus:[60] "If a single private corporation could own the whole Tennessee watershed, it would naturally provide as many different services as could be produced from the river, collecting its charges for these services in various ways according to circumstances. Navigation privileges, water supplies, electricity would be sold directly to consumers; flood control and less tangible benefits would appear as increased rental values of real estate. In this way many services that could not be made profitable as separate business enterprises would be profitable if combined into a single trust. No such all-embracing private trust is likely to be allowed in our democratic system. The only all-embracing organisation is democracy itself. The people own the undivided rights in the Tennessee valley as well as in the rest of the nation. A job such as taming the Tennessee River, which is too big for a private corporation, must be managed by the agents of the people if it is to be done at all."

Throughout the industrial world for the last fifty years, the units in which business and manufacture is organised have been growing larger and larger, until there are now many world-wide concerns with almost absolute powers within their field. It seems reasonably certain that this process must continue; it is dictated by technical advances, whose full benefit can only be reaped if they are used on a large and comprehensive scale. The economic organisation of the world is going totalitarian, and nothing can stop it, except perhaps a return to handicraft methods of production only capable of supporting a smaller population. What will happen to human freedom during this change? Must a realistic view of the world accept it as inevitable that as production becomes more organised men must also be regimented under central control, and thus lose their liberty?

Freedom is a very troublesome concept for the scientist to discuss, partly because he is not convinced that, in the last analysis, there is such a thing. Science works by discovering causes, and it finds difficulty in admitting that there is a free will, or desires and impulses which have no underlying cause. But leaving such philosophical questions on one side, science recognises that there is a feeling of freedom which men have, and that when they protest against the danger of losing their freedom they are not just talking hot air.

The "freedom" men talk of really covers three or four different things. There is the freedom of not being restrained by law from doing certain things if one wants to; there is the freedom of being enabled to do one's best, to show initiative and to contribute something of one's own to society; and there is the freedom to be odd, to disagree with the majority and go one's own way.

The first freedom everyone recognises to be more or less of a farce at the present time. We are all free to dine at the most expensive hotels, to get the most highly-valued education society provides at the most fashionable public schools of England or private schools of America, to set up in business as a newspaper proprietor. Perfectly free to do so— if we have the wherewithal. The legal freedom to do such things is better than being prohibited from doing them, but it is not enough in itself. It has practical importance only if there is an opportunity to take advantage of it. As was said above, science is definite that ability is so widely spread in the community that it would be to the community's advantage to spread opportunity equally widely. Many more than half the able people in the country do not get a satisfactory training or scope for their talents, though there is no law against it. Their theoretical freedom will have to be made practical if this wastage is to be avoided.

The encouragement of initiative in an organised society is a more difficult proposition. I think nobody would question that it is desirable. But it is often argued that any Governmental or central control invariably leads to all the faults of bureaucracy—red tape and timid mediocrity. The question is usually discussed as though bureaucracy automatically went with public ownership, and efficiency with ownership by private business, but it is difficult to believe that the connection is really direct. It seems more likely that it is a matter of the size of the organisation; if it is too big for the efforts of an individual man to be noticed, there is no incentive for him to do his best. If the trend towards monopoly or totalitarian organisation continues, this will be the state of all production, equally whether in private or public hands. But there is no reason to suppose that the difficulty is insuperable. In Germany, for instance, some of the public enterprises such as the new auto-roads showed at least as much boldness in conception and efficiency in execution as any private concern would have produced. And in America some of the big monopolies, such as the American Telephone and Telegraph, are as competent and up-to-date as anyone could wish. In fact, the most far-reaching and the most audacious of recent enterprises have, in actual fact, mostly been carried out not by private enterprise but by governments. For instance, the provision of stable civil government, and the largest irrigation system in the world, in the British India that was, or the development of the atomic bomb in the United States.

Probably there are two main factors to bear in mind when trying to combine initiative with large-scale organisation. If the community as a whole values and insists on efficiency, it will probably get it. Americans really believe whole-heartedly in having gadgets that work, and the A.T. & T., monopoly though it is, is a part of American society and shares the belief.

Perhaps it is a more important point that men seem not to put out their best unless they have competition. But the competition need not be for private profit, as it is to-day. Most people who can show initiative and drive enjoy doing so, and can be tempted to do so if success will bring them greater scope. They can compete for a wider field of action; in fact, even now this is probably a considerably more important psychological motive for efficiency in business than simple profit-making. The giants of industry, the tycoons as America calls them, have mostly long ago earned more than they can possibly spend; they keep on because they are interested, and it is a subsidiary fact that the only way they can keep on is to continue to make profits, which are not their primary motive. There is no reason why competition for scope should not be combined with large-scale organisation, even if competition for profit cannot be.

It might be claimed, however, that the freedom to compete with one's fellows, and to show initiative in doing so, is a comparatively superficial matter, appealing only to those tough types who worship success. The true freedom, to some people, is essentially a private and internal affair. It is the opportunity to express in work whatever of creative urge one may possess. The essential thing for this type of freedom is that a man's daily activities should not only call on him continually to decide for himself what he should do to carry out his task, but should do this in a sphere exacting enough to bring out the best of which he is capable. This "freedom for creativity" is much greater in some of the handicraft activities, such as farming, carpentry, even bricklaying, than it is in most jobs on a mechanised mass-production line. It is worth noting how completely it is distinct and separate from many of the other concepts also called "freedom"; the workmen who sculptured the mediæval cathedrals had plenty of scope for their creative instincts, but very little to question the dogmas of the Church or to win "success" by changing their economic status.

Freedom for creation is one of the deepest and most important social ideals. People who resent the limitations on it which have undoubtedly followed the industrial revolution often blame this result on the scientists, who invented the industrial techniques; forgetting that it was not the scientists, but the industrial magnates and the bureaucrats who organised how these techniques should be put into operation. Actually science is itself one of the most essentially creative activities; it is comparable in this to painting, writing and the other arts. The men who carry forward the work of science are as little likely as any group in the modern world to undervalue the freedom to create. In a world run according to scientific ideals, the most important objective would be to encourage all those faculties in which man has evolved furthest ahead of the other animals; and the capacity for creative achievement is the most outstanding of these.

The last sort of freedom, the freedom to be odd and unlike one's neighbour, is not, I think, a scientific value; at least I should not like to have to produce scientific reasons why a community which allowed it must be better for its members than one which did not. In the extraordinary variety of societies studied by anthropologists, some allow much more latitude to individuals than others, and it is not clear that the laxer ones are usually the more successful. In fact, Unwin[61] has recently argued the exact opposite—that too great freedom, particularly sexual freedom, lowers the energy and drive available for the important tasks of the community. I think he has hardly made out his case, although it is probably true that there is some limit beyond which it is not desirable to go in permitting people to do what they like regardless of what their neighbours think. But, at any rate in England and America, people value very highly their liberty to go their own way. Even if there is no particular scientific reason to support them, scientists are bound to be very sympathetic to such an ideal, because within their own technical field freedom to differ from the majority is one of the essential conditions of their work. Once destroy the freedom for any scientist to disagree with the majority, including his elders and betters, and scientific progress would come to a fairly immediate end. What scientists need and can give good reasons for in their own special field, they are not likely to want to deny to society as a whole in its more general affairs.

Science is often accused of being responsible for war, and that from two different angles. The less bitter accusation is that science, by providing the world with more devastating and efficient machinery, has increased the horror and beastliness of the wars which men have always engaged in. To a certain extent this is true; in so far as science increases man's power, it has enabled him to deliver heavier blows. But it is only fair to point out that it also strengthens his defence. War to-day extends over a wider area and involves more people than the wars of the past, but the armies suffered a very low proportion of casualties in comparison with the magnitude of the effects obtained. The most appalling slaughter was caused by the mass extermination of civilians, primarily in Eastern Europe, for which relatively primitive methods could be, and largely were, employed.

There is no denying that technical developments have brought war back again to civilians and women and children. These did not escape in uncivilised wars, such as the raids of Attila and his Huns, nor in more or less anarchic civil wars, such as those of the French and Russian Revolutions, but for most of the last few hundred years warfare has been in an intermediate stage of technical development which confined its effects to the actual combatant troops. Most people have therefore acquired the feeling that it is less brutalising to kill a man in uniform than a woman in ordinary clothes, although the more militant feminists point out, perhaps rightly, that this feeling is really a relic of the days when women were considered the weaker vessel, and valuable articles of property. But if it is actually a backward step to bring war home to the whole population instead of only to the soldiers, it must be admitted that it is the development of more scientific methods of war which has brought this about. And it is possible that modern war, even if less destructive of life, is more devastating in its effects on other human values than were the wars of the past.

The development of the atomic bomb, and still more of

bacteriological warfare, will almost certainly make this situation look very differently in the future. There can now, I think, be little doubt that these scientific "advances" have outstripped defence methods so far as to make possible vastly greater casualties and far greater destruction of material resources than before; and if defence measures are attempted against them, these are likely to involve very great disturbance of normal civilised life. While it is clear that the general body of scientists must take a great deal of responsibility in this connection—and particularly, as I argue above on p. 32, for the positive action required to control the new weapons—yet it would not be fair that they should carry all the odium for having introduced these horrors. The scientists who produced the weapons did so under the orders of the authorities properly constituted by society. Their responsibility was, on the face of it, exactly similar to that of the bomber crews who executed the area bombing of German cities—a policy which, on military grounds, was open to grave and, in my not very well informed opinion, probably decisive objection. The only grounds on which more blame could be given to the scientists than to the aircrew would be that scientists should be social leaders who cannot evade the duty of providing more definite guidance than is expected from ordinary man—and this is a thesis which is not generally accepted.

The accusation of increasing the horror of war is sometimes reinforced by a second, that science actually justifies war and endorses it as an essential part of human activity. Science is alleged to believe that all evolutionary advance proceeds through the struggle for survival, and to look upon war as the most decisive expression of this struggle among men. Both Nazis and Fascists made this claim, although the Nazis tended to justify war more as the final expression of man's service to the State than as a test of his individual worth. But Mussolini expressed the argument very plainly in his article on Fascism in the *Italian Encyclopædia*:[62] "Above all,

Fascism, in so far as it considers and observes the future and development of humanity quite apart from the political considerations of the moment, believes neither in the possibility nor in the utility of perpetual peace. . . . War alone brings up to their highest tension all human energies, and puts the stamp of nobility upon the peoples who have the courage to meet it."

The argument is based on a complete misunderstanding of the scientific theory of evolution. The phrase "struggle for existence" is a catchy slogan put over by Darwin, who was a genius at popularisation; but it is not to be taken literally. If a few thousand acorns start sprouting in the underbrush of a wood, there is a "struggle for existence" between them, but they do not get up and hit one another over the head. The struggle is metaphorical, and the scientific doctrine of natural selection gives no direct sanction to human war as a method of evolution.

Leaving the general theory of evolution, and going into more detail about man's nature, it is obvious that he is not a vegetable, and does not, and should not, behave like an oak seedling. He seems to be naturally a pretty active creature, and, like other active mammals, only does well if given a chance to use his powers to the full. But the other animals for which this is true do not in general go to war, and do not evolve through its effects. Individuals may sometimes fight among themselves, but the main "struggle" is against things of a different kind; to escape from other animals who prey on them, or to catch other animals to eat, or to deal more successfully with the inanimate world. There is no reason from natural history why man, simply because he is the sort of creature who must be doing something active, must band together in groups to kill other men. In fact, anthropologists know of tribes to whom the idea has never occurred. "I myself," says Ruth Benedict,[63] "tried to talk of warfare to the Mission Indians of California, but it was impossible. Their misunderstanding of warfare was abysmal. They did not have the basis in their own culture upon which the idea could exist, and their attempts to reason it out reduced the great wars to which we are able to dedicate ourselves with moral fervour to the level of alley brawls. They did not happen to have a cultural pattern which distinguished between them."

Far from considering war as the highest activity of man, or even as an inescapable trait in human nature, scientists, even more than most people in this country, find it a damnable, if unavoidable, interruption of their serious business. For science is concerned with man's real evolutionary advance, with giving him the mastery over things which will enable him to translate his wishes and aspirations into fact, and to overcome the obstacles which prevent the full development of his nature. This mastery can only be increased by fuller knowledge and understanding. The world is a safe which cannot be cracked by a sledge-hammer; one has to learn the codes which open the locks. It is only a hindrance, and not a way of advance, if the safe-breakers start fighting, or if, when the door is beginning to open, someone stands in the way to prevent the others going in.

These two points—that the "struggle for existence" is a more subtle process than its name might suggest, and that man's behaviour cannot be thought of as a mere animal fighting—were clearly recognised by one of Darwin's most penetrating contemporaries. I like to picture him riding to hounds near Manchester, hat crammed well down, red beard blown back against his muddy pink, and thinking up some crack about the surplus theory of value; he was Frederick Engels, a bad 'un to beat. He pointed out that, as well as a selection due to the pressure of over-population, there is a selection by greater capacity of adaptation; and he drew attention to the fact that the crude idea of the struggle for existence was a reflection of current social theories into natural history and could not then be brought back again into sociology as an independent argument for competitive capitalism or for war. "The whole Darwinian theory of the struggle for life is simply the transference from society to organic nature of Hobbes' theory of *bellum omnium contra omnes*, and of the bourgeois economic theory of competition, as well as the Malthusian theory of population. When once this feat has been accomplished . . . it is very easy to transfer these theories back again from natural history to the history of society, and altogether too naïve to maintain that thereby these assertions have been proved as eternal natural laws of society. . . . Darwin did not know what a bitter satire he wrote on mankind, and especially on his countrymen, when he showed that free competition, which the economists celebrate as the highest historical achievement, is the normal state of the *animal* kingdom."[64]

CHAPTER X

BELIEVING IN SCIENCE

THERE is one human characteristic which to-day can find
a mode of expression in nationalism and war, and which, it
may seem, would have to be completely denied in a scientific
society. That is the tendency to find some dogma to which
can be attached complete belief, forthright and unquestioning.
That men do experience a need for certainty of such a kind
can scarcely be doubted. As Voltaire pointed out, if God
did not exist man would have to invent him. And there is
certainly a difficulty for science here, since scientific belief is
a quantitative affair; one believes in some things more, in
others less, but in none with such absoluteness that evidence
becomes irrelevant. How, then, can believing man be at
home in a sceptical scientific world?

The problem arises on two scales, as it were. To take the
minor one first: many people have the impression that scientific statements are always intolerably cautious, hedging and
stuck-in-the-mud. It apparently seems impossible to them
that anything of moment can be concealed within the heavy
sentences of the conventional scientific vernacular. The
opening phrases: "While it is idle to speculate, the available
evidence may be taken to indicate . . ." or "The possibility
must, it appears, be envisaged . . ."—serve like the slime of
an oyster to slip them down the gullet unchewed and hardly
tasted. But the answer to this is simply a jeering "Think
again." The wary circumspection is called for precisely because the ideas which science advances are so outrageous.
While the orthodox held, with confident certainty, a theory
of dreams which must have been a bore already to the
Pharaoh's courtiers in the time of Joseph, science hesitantly

insinuated the devastating notion of the unconscious mind. It is passionately debated whether or not we can, after death, make tables go bump; and meanwhile the geneticists point out that anyone who is succeeded by an unbroken line of descendants is assured of the material immortality of some of his essential substance, his genes (apart from the uncontrollable process of mutation), but that the quantity is halved in each generation and there is no way of determining which half is preserved; and the tissue-culturist can promise, with his hand on his heart, but touching wood with one little finger, to provide actual immortality of the flesh (of some parts and only in bits). It is not the caution with which they are advanced which makes such scientific results seem unexciting; it is that they are too fantastically out of line with our cultural traditions to register.

Moreover, the nearer it gets to action, the more specific, though not necessarily the more unqualified, the advice of science becomes. When it comes to a practical matter of eating, Professor Haldane[65] consumes no more than three ounces of baking soda at a sitting, betting on the current physiological theory that that quantity would alter the acidity of his blood just less than the amount required to kill him; his colleagues could argue disinterestedly the likelihood of the theory proving inadequate. What science gives one is a specific and detailed instruction which has a probability of bringing about the desired result; and scientific action is normally and essentially based on probabilities rather than on certainties.

That would be true of its action in social matters also. The evidence that improved education and nutrition would raise the general intelligence of the lower-paid strata of society is not unassailable; but it is strong enough to make that view probable enough to be a basis for action, and science would not only unhesitatingly act on it, if it had the power, but must insist that a failure to do so is a gross betrayal of scientific ethics.

The odds at which an experiment becomes worth trying depend on how much harm it can do if it goes wrong, and especially on its liability to get out of control. It is this consideration which forces science to be unquestionably on the side of democracy. In a social experiment, which is performed in order to improve the lot of the members of the society, it is they, the experimental material, who must be the judges of whether the experiment is a success, and the ultimate agents who decide whether it should continue or not. Neither scientists nor any other particular group of people can decide it for them; the scientists' function is to suggest changes worth trying and to point out benefits which the general populace may have overlooked.

But it is enough to be definite without being certain? The major objection to scientific scepticism is to its fundamental uncertainty. People may be willing to bet on a probability when things are going well, but when the world seems against them, and they are depressed and unhappy, they tend to turn for comfort to something which they feel they can believe in without reservations. This desire for an ultimate bedrock of stability—for something which, instead of being at the mercy of the mere chance happenings of the world, stands outside them, uninfluenced and constant—is a very important element in man's nature. It is often argued that it is so powerful that it is bound to frustrate any attempt to base a society on an empirical, sceptical attitude. It is pointed out that in Russia after the revolution the peasants and common people, though on the whole not unwilling to give up their belief in the God of the Orthodox Church, did not remain free-thinking, but proceeded to canonise Lenin and pay their devotions to him. And one of the most fundamental troubles of Europe, as was pointed out earlier, is the lack of any secure system of beliefs on which people can rely. Is science, for all its logical consistency, in a position to satisfy this primary need of man?

Nowadays, mainly through the efforts of psycho-analysts,

we know something about the psychological nature of the need to believe. Every human being starts life in complete dependence on its parents, and under their absolute control. The most important process in development is the movement away from reliance on the power and protection of the parents, and the acquisition of the capacity to deal with circumstances unaided. No one, at the present stage of human evolution, completes this movement. No one entirely escapes from the loving, commanding parent, who becomes built up into the structure of a man's mind under the disguise of a conscience or a God; who remains something which one can, perhaps, disobey, but whose power, such as it is, does not derive from this world, but is primary and unquestionable, standing outside the world and coming before it.

In the normal man this external authority, or super-ego, as it is called, is counterbalanced and checked by the rational part of the mind, which is developed to handle the outside world. There is little doubt that the direction of evolution is towards a restriction of the importance of the super-ego, and an increase in the power and freedom of reason. But the factors which determine the relative strengths of these two aspects of the human mind are not of a kind which one can expect to change very rapidly. One could not abolish the super-ego by teaching children a set of ideas different to those they learn at present. The only hope of doing so would be by a complete change in the whole nature of the relationship between parents and children, which would not be at all easy to bring about.

It seems, then, that we have to reckon with a tendency of mankind to make themselves a super-ego which they can, from time to time when it suits them, believe in with an unreasoning devotion. But the substitute father may take many different forms; if it cannot be God it may be Lenin. Its nature is by no means an unimportant matter, and is probably much more easy to influence than its existence. It may be jealous, mysterious and violently opposed to reason; but it might, on the other hand, be wise, tolerant and more reasonable than our weak minds can imitate; it might be that very process of evolution whose direction determines science's ethical attitude. There need, in fact, be no irreconcilable conflict between the rational and irrational parts of man's mind; he can have an unreasonable belief in the value of reason.

It is therefore quite possible for man's irrational impulse to find a way of satisfying itself even in a scientific society. The scoffer suggests that, however empirical and objective the society claims to be, one will discover that faith has put in an appearance in it. But the reply is, What of it? Why shouldn't it be a helpful faith?

A scientific society, however, would not be founded on faith. The super-ego would be the interloper. Most societies of the past have, I think, claimed the opposite, that they are based on a religious doctrine. It was an emotional belief in feudal Christianity which held the mediæval world together; which laid down the rules which prevented the wars from being too devastating, kept economic power within bounds by the doctrine of the "just price," and determined the structure of society in the hierarchy stretching from the King, God's Anointed, to the lowest villein. But a glance at the history books will convince anyone that the super-ego did not have it all its own way. Plenty of men laid their beliefs on one side and used their wits to look after their own interests. In fact, if they had not done so, civilisation would have remained static and fixed for ever in the shape it had when the beliefs were consolidated.

The mediæval world was one theoretically founded on irrational beliefs, and in practice considerably invaded by empirical reason. A scientific world would be the other way round; theoretically based on empiricism, in practice undoubtedly entertaining many unproved beliefs. Its great advantage would lie in the fact that it is to the application of reason to the external world that civilised man owes his evolution from the savage. In societies founded on emotional beliefs, reason has to fight bitterly for recognition, let alone for power to put its conclusions into practice. In a scientific world this same reason, the only method of human progress, would have become the officially recognised basis of the whole social scheme.

When one looks towards a scientific society, and considers how the super-ego can be accommodated and made use of within it, it is necessary to realise that we are at present in a very bad situation in this respect. Our great-grandfathers pictured their super-egos in terms of a God. They might, and frequently did, disobey his authority; he might be jealous, narrow-minded, cruel and generally disagreeable, although he might also be just and loving; but whatever his characteristics, a God has a certain scale. He is never simply mean, dingy and crotchety. And he dwells comfortably far away, and can be disregarded, when necessary, with comparative impunity.

Modern man seems in danger of losing both these advantages. The symbolic parent, whose authority we fear, is usually not called a God at all these days, and certainly does not deserve the title. The bogey that dominated the inter-war years was a much more bloodless creature—an old grey man muttering to his cronies in a club, a disapproving neighbour peeping through the curtains. It is called They—They won't like that, They won't approve, They don't do it like that, They say that's Bolshie. And They are essentially impersonal, negative, nondescript and incredibly suspicious. Their quiet, insinuating voice recommends firmly against action, except sometimes when they approve a violent expression of hatred. No thunderbolts issue from Their Olympus, only solicitor's letters warning against the consequences of pursuing the contemplated line of action; They are as unjovial as any gods could be.

That sort of a super-ego would be no good to a scientific

society. It is not true, whatever you may have been led to believe, that the progress of science demands that everyone should always be right, and no society which takes caution as its main virtue will get anywhere, however scientific its thinking. But the pendulum seems to be already swinging away from Them, towards some new and livelier embodiment of authority.

It is, as They would be the first to point out, extremely hazardous to speculate on what kind of super-ego we shall make for ourselves in Their place. But even They might almost approve the conventional suggestion that we must be ready for the pendulum to swing to the opposite extreme. Are we in for a Romantic Revival? for one of those apparently paradoxical periods when the super-ego lends its authority to an ideal which emphasises spontaneity and naturalness? There is some evidence which can be interpreted in that way. It can be found in the cultural sphere. Painters, like John Piper, who were most conscious of the need to find some more solid "tree in the field," are tending to go in that direction, to paint pictures in which the prime aim is romance, and the purely æsthetic advances of the abstract period are of secondary importance, incorporated where possible, but left to look after themselves. Poets like MacNiece defy Them:[66]

> "No.
> You cannot argue with the eyes or voice;
> Argument will frustrate you till you die,
> But go your own way, give the voice the lie,
> Outstare the inhuman eyes. That is the way.
> Go back to where you came from and do not keep
> Crossing the road to escape them, do not avoid the ambush,
> Take sly detours, but ride the pass direct."

These are only hints, indications of a possible trend which opinion may take. My guess—and, I confess, my hope—is that they need to be taken seriously. For I do not think that an increase in the importance of a romantic view of life would make it any more difficult to achieve a scientific society. The substitution of a romantic ideal for our recent pallid and inhibited one would, I think, in itself simply release enormous potentialities of action which have been suppressed. It would be incompatible with the myriad vested interests, large and small, which sat on our heads like tin-pot or cast-iron lids. They would go flying.

The important question is what would emerge, and that would depend on what kind of romantic ideal we had adopted. As I pointed out before, almost any kind of ideal can be twisted to serve as the basis of a Fascist system. Not every kind is suitable for a scientific society; no anti-intellectual ideal would serve. But science has plenty of romance of its own to offer. In fact, its romance is so obvious and outstanding that it is traditionally the first enthusiasm of boys; to become an engine-driver used to be a child's first choice, nowadays perhaps to become a pilot. And the possibilities which science is opening up are so manifold and so large in scope that an enthusiasm of the same kind could provide the most important practical aims for a grown-up man; to take a responsible part in the carrying out of a great scientific enterprise, such as the development of the Tennessee valley, with its dams and power-houses and the social organisation which goes with them, would be no mean or uninspiring objective. Or if we wish to consider the matter in less immediate and concrete terms, I have already in an earlier chapter pointed out that science is not ethically neutral; it does imply a certain type of moral outlook. It has, in fact, something to say about the most important questions of the world, and it could therefore be a candidate for the position of super-ego.

The argument, like all good arguments in this finite world, has come back from the other side to the point it started from. I had suggested that one might have a scientific society, officially based on the practice of empirical reason; but I argued that the other side of man's nature would have to be satisfied by a belief in some authority, a thrill for some romance. We have now reached the conclusion that science can also provide this thrill and this authority. Science by itself is able to provide mankind with a way of life which is, firstly self-consistent and harmonious, and, secondly, free for the exercise of that objective reason on which our material progress depends. So far as I can see the scientific attitude of mind is the only one which is, at the present day, adequate in both these respects. There are many other worthy ideals which might supplement it; but I cannot see that any of them could take its place as the basis of a progressing and rich society.

SUMMARY

THE civilisation of the last few centuries is disintegrating; it suffered a stroke in 1914 and has been moribund ever since. It served its members indirectly, relying on the half-understood laws of private profit and supply and demand, and its whole system of beliefs and values was appropriate to such a mechanism. The type of economic system which will replace it is already clear in outline: it will be centralised, and totalitarian in the sense that all the major aspects of the economic development of large regions are consciously planned as an integrated whole. What is not clear is the character of the social ideals and values which will determine the purposes for which the system will be used.

The Nazi and Fascist totalitarian systems were fundamentally pointless; apart from the simple ideal of increasing the power already in the hands of a certain clique, they point to no ultimate direction for human striving. To the man left isolated in the world by the disappearance of the traditions he relied on, they offer only the gimcrack comfort of a rigmarole of emotive words; blood, soil, the Fascist spirituality. They would use the economic evolution towards an organised society to bring about a cultural regression to the Stone Age; and this is inevitable in any society in which a totalitarian economic system is used primarily for the benefit of a restricted group.

The application of conscious control to the economic functioning of society is actually a step forward along the path of man's evolutionary advance. Throughout the whole history of life on the earth science observes an increase in the accuracy with which animals can perceive their surroundings, and a progressive development of the brain structures which enable them to reach a practical understanding of it. This general trend defines the direction which is forwards. It does more: it makes clear the method by which advance can be brought about—by action based on sensitive examination of the facts and rational inference from them. The mastery of this method is not child's play; it is the ideal of scientific culture.

The inter-war period has been a time of pupation; the capitalist world has been in the chrysalis of the Great Depression, breaking down its caterpillar economics and culture and preparing to emerge as a quite different-looking butterfly. The artists and writers who have been busy liquidating the outworn traditions have not formulated at all clearly the new culture which will succeed them. But the only part of their work which seems constructive and progressive is derived, unconsciously and tortuously it may be, from the scientific attitude. This is an attitude whose final standard of value is an observed process of evolutionary advance; it judges things not "for themselves," but only for the effects which they produce on the rate of advance; no other considerations are relevant, however much traditional emotion may be attached to them. From this standpoint, the good of a society is measured by the good of its individual members; no special importance attaches to the welfare of particular groups, such as the present property owners, and none at all to that of abstract entities such as "The State."

The rational economic system, at whose birth pangs we are already assisting, can only be fully utilised if it is infused by a culture whose method of approach is also rational, intelligent and empirical. Prim Science has so far neglected to confess to the world that he has begotten such an offspring on the harlot Humanities; but the infant culture is beginning to peep already—in its bastard vigour lies the only hope for an heir worthy of the civilisations of the past.

LIST OF REFERENCES

1 Technological Trends and National Policy. U.S. Govt. Printing Office. 1937; p. 65.
2 Margaret Mead, *Sex and Temperament*, Routledge, 1935; pp. 111 *seq.* and 279.
3 Cf. R. M. Titmus, *Poverty and Population*, Macmillan, 1938; p. 86.
4 See *Science and Ethics*, ed. by C. H. Waddington, Allen & Unwin, 1942.
4a Pablo Picasso, from a conversation with Christian Zervos, published in English translation in *The Painter's Object*, edited by Myfanwy Evans, Gerald Howe, 1937 (one of the few books about painting written by painters).
5 T. S. Eliot, The Love-Song of J. Alfred Prufrock, from *Poems 1905-1925*, Faber & Gwyer, 1926.
6 T. S. Eliot, Preludes I, from *Poems*.
7 T. S. Eliot, The Waste Land.
8 E. E. Cummings, One 2, from *Is. 5*, Boni & Liveright, New York, 1926.
9 E. E. Cummings, Five 2, from *Is. 5*.
10 T. S. Eliot, Animula.
11 John Piper, *The Painter's Object*; p. 69.
12 Paul Nash, *The Painter's Object*; p. 108.
13 Max Ernst, *The Painter's Object*; p. 79.
14 Pablo Picasso, *The Painter's Object*; p. 81.
15 Aldous Huxley, from *Leda*, Chatto & Windus, 1920.
16 W. H. Auden, from *Another Time*, Faber & Faber, 1940; p. 70.
17 William Empson, Invitation to Juno, from *Poems*, Chatto & Windus, 1935.
18 William Empson, from *Poems*.
19 Stephen Spender, The Indifferent One, from *The Still Centre*, Faber & Faber, 1939.
20 Cecil Day Lewis, from *The Magnetic Mountain*, Hogarth Press, 1930; p. 18.
21 Cecil Day Lewis, *The Magnetic Mountain*; p. 34.
22 John Crowe Ransom, from *Two Gentlemen in Bonds*, Knopf, New York, 1927.
23 Salvador Dali, from *La Conquête de l'Irrationnel*, Editions Surréalistes, Paris, 1935.
24 T. S. Eliot, *East Coker*, Faber & Faber, 1940.
25 W. H. Auden, from *Another Time*.

26 T. S. Eliot, from *East Coker*.
27 W. H. Auden, from *Another Time*.
28 Marcel Breuer, in *Circle*, Faber & Faber, 1937; p. 193.
29 J. L. Martin, in *Circle*, p. 215.
30 Raymond B. Fosdick, *The Rockefeller Foundation—A Review for 1939*. New York.
31 Robert S. Lynd, *Knowledge for What?* Princeton Univ. Press, 1939; p. 8.
32 A. V. Hill, *Nature*, 1933; p. 952.
33 R. S. Lynd, *Knowledge for What?* p. 6.
34 See *The Middlesbrough Survey & Plan*, by Max Lock and others. Published Middlesbrough Corporation, 1947.
35 A. V. Hill, *Cambridge Review*, Nov. 8th, 1940.
36 Erich Kästner, Ein Mann Gibt Auskunft, from book of the same name, Deutsche Verlags Anstalt, Stuttgart, 1930.
37 Rainer Maria Rilke, from *Requiem für Eine Freundin*.
38 E. Krieck, quoted by Robert A. Brady, *The Spirit and Structure of German Fascism*. Gollancz, 1937; p. 60.
39 B. Mussolini. *The Doctrine of Fascism*, publ. in *Enciclopedia Italiana*, 1932; English translation in *Social and Political Doctrines of Contemporary Europe*, by M. Oakeshott, Cambridge University Press, 1939; p. 164.
40 Bernhard Rust, quoted by Brady, p. 51.
41 J. B. S. Haldane, *The Marxist Philosophy and the Sciences*, Allen & Unwin, 1938; p. 16.
42 *e.g.* J. B. S. Haldane, *Ibid.*, p. 14.
43 V. I. Lenin, *Materialism and Empirio-criticism*, quoted by Haldane in reference (41).
44 A. N. Whitehead, *The Concept of Nature*, Cambridge Univ. Press, 1920.
45 Quoted by Haldane in reference (41).
46 J. B. S. Haldane, *Heredity and Politics*, Allen & Unwin, 1938; p. 126.
47 Robert S. Lynd, *Knowledge for What?* p. 66.
48 Ditto; p. 60.
49 See G. Bateson, *Naven*, Cambridge University Press, 1936.
50 From a preliminary report by Tom Harrisson.
51 L. F. Richardson, Generalised Foreign Politics, *British Journal of Psychology Monograph*, 1939.
52 Kenneth Fearing, from C Stands for Civilisation in *Dead Reckoning*, Random House, New York, 1938.
53 Ruth Benedict, *Patterns of Culture*, Routledge, New York, 1933; p. 273.

54   G. Bateson, *Naven*, and *Culture Contact and Schismogenesis*, from
     Man, 1935; p. 199.
55   See the studies of Gray and Moshinsky, published in *Political
     Arithmetic*, edited by L. Hogben, Allen & Unwin, 1938.
56   Ruth Benedict, *Patterns of Culture*, p. 16.
57   Gregory Bateson and Margaret Mead, *Balinese Character*, New
     York Academy of Sciences, 1942.
58   Charles and Moshinsky, in *Political Arithmetic*; p. 159.
59   Lewis Mumford, *The Culture of Cities*, Harcourt Brace, New
     York, 1938; p. 258.
60   T. V. A. Pamphlet, *To Keep the Water in the Rivers and the Soil
     on the Land*, U.S. Govt. Printing Office, 1938; p. 5.
61   J. D. Unwin, *Hopousia, or the sexual and economic foundations of
     a new society*, Allen & Unwin, 1940.
62   B. Mussolini, *The Doctrine of Fascism*; p. 170.
63   Ruth Benedict, *Patterns of Culture*; p. 31.
64   Frederick Engels, *The Dialectics of Nature*, translated by Clemens
     Dutt, Lawrence and Wishart, 1940; pp. 19, 208, 236.
65   J. B. S. Haldane, see On Being one's own Rabbit, in *Possible
     Worlds*.
66   Louis MacNiece from "Eclogue in Iceland", in *The Earth Compels*,
     1938; p. 38.

PENGUIN SCIENCE NEWS
Edited by John Enogat

The influence of Scientists and their work on our every-day lives is a truth that is incessantly brought home to the reading man. Scientific research is now applied as much to the food productive capacities of the soil as to the atom bomb. *Penguin Science News*, appearing at regular intervals, is designed to give up-to-date information on these matters. The treatment of the subjects is as acceptable to the layman as to the student, and every issue contains a photogravure section which illustrates the matters dealt with.

The Press has said on this series:

The Penguin Books have been one of the most brilliant inspirations and services given to the English-reading world during the last ten years. They have distributed good and appropriate books in millions, and have made a major contribution to the education of modern democracy. Their latest venture is the launching of a series of quarterly booklets on Science News. Nothing could be more appropriate at the present time. – *The Listener*.

Penguin Books also publish

NEW BIOLOGY
Edited by M. L. Johnson and Michael Abercrombie

This series is published at regular intervals, and, to quote the editors: '. . . is a miscellany of essays, each an up-to-date account of some aspects of biology which has excited contemporary interest . . .' Although it is mainly for readers with some scientific knowledge, the subjects are presented lucidly and plainly, in such a way that a non-scientific reader can follow. Each issue contains gravure illustrations and a glossary of the scientific terms used.